SECRETS OF
THE MOON

SECRETS OF THE MOON

Understanding and Analysing the Lunar Surface

Gilbert Fielder

CRC Press
Taylor & Francis Group
Boca Raton London New York

CRC Press is an imprint of the
Taylor & Francis Group, an **informa** business

First edition published 2022
by CRC Press
6000 Broken Sound Parkway NW, Suite 300, Boca Raton, FL 33487-2742

and by CRC Press
2 Park Square, Milton Park, Abingdon, Oxon, OX14 4RN

Library of Congress Cataloging-in-Publication Data
Names: Fielder, Gilbert, author.
Title: Secrets of the moon : understanding and analysing the lunar surface / Gilbert Fielder.
Description: First edition. | Boca Raton : CRC Press, 2022. | Includes bibliographical references and index.
Identifiers: LCCN 2021032689 (print) | LCCN 2021032690 (ebook) | ISBN 9781032011059 (hardback) | ISBN 9781032019857 (paperback) | ISBN 9781003181279 (ebook)
Subjects: LCSH: Moon--Surface.
Classification: LCC QB591 .F496 2022 (print) | LCC QB591 (ebook) | DDC 559/.91--dc23
LC record available at https://lccn.loc.gov/2021032689
LC ebook record available at https://lccn.loc.gov/2021032690

ISBN: 978-1-032-01105-9 (hbk)
ISBN: 978-1-032-01985-7 (pbk)
ISBN: 978-1-003-18127-9 (ebk)

DOI: 10.1201/9781003181279

Typeset in Times
by MPS Limited, Dehradun

To Jane, Clare and Lynne

Contents

Preface   xi
Acknowledgements   xiii
Author Bio   xv

1 **Preparatory Studies**   1

2 **Studies at Manchester and the Pic du Midi**   7

3 **Wrinkle Ridges**   13

4 **The Straight Wall**   17

5 **Thoughts on Mare Imbrium**   25

6 **The Apparent Acceleration of the Moon**   31

7 **The Slowing Rotation of the Earth**   33

8 **The Receding Moon**   37

9 **Distorted Craters**   39

10 **The Lunar Grid System**   43

11 **Mapping the Grid around the Whole of the Moon**   49

12 **Faulting and the Rotation of the Moon**   53

13 **The Origin of the Lunar Grid System**   59

14 **Melting in the Moon**   63

15 **The Origin of the Moon**   65

16 **Fine Lineaments and Their Significance**   67

17 **The Ages of the Lunar Surface Features**   77

18   The Origins of Small Craters   81

19   The Proportion of Endocraters to Impact Craters   93

20   The Origin of Crater-Chains in Grid Fractures   97

21   The Origins of Small Craters in a Lunar Lava Flow   99

22   Small Double Craters   107

23   Double Craters and the Depth and Compaction of the Regolith   109

24   Dating the Mare Flows   111

25   Studies of Large Craters   113

26   The Ray-Craters Tycho, Copernicus and Aristarchus   115

27   Unexpected Volcanic Flows in Tycho and Aristarchus   121

28   Volcanic Tumuli on the Floor of Tycho   125

29   The Unusual Rocks of Tycho, Copernicus and Aristarchus   129

30   Cracks in Tycho and Kilauea   131

31   Central Peaks and the Impact Process   133

32   The Crater Aristarchus   139

33   The Crater Copernicus   143

34   Dating the Lavas of Tycho and Aristarchus   145

35   The Origin of the Lavas in Impact Craters   149

36   Tensions in the Lunar Crust   153

37   Is There Any Current Volcanic Activity on the Moon?   161

38   Maria, Rilles and Wrinkle Ridges   163

39   Maria and Mascons   177

40   Ghost Craters and Elementary Rings   181

41 The Nature of the Lamont Complex   189

42 Terrestrial Ring Complexes and Their Origin   193

43 Are There Ring Dykes on the Moon?   199

44 The Origins of Large Lunar Craters in General   205

45 Return to the Moon   209

References   213
Glossary   217
Index   225

Preface

It is well known that craters of a variety of shapes and sizes occur on our natural satellite, but the Moon is also traversed by deep fractures which present, on the surface, as lineaments (principally, linear ridges, troughs and chains of craters). The gross lineaments have dimensions of the order of tens of kilometres and may be noticed using Earth-based telescopes or telescopic photographs. At the other end of the scale, close-up photographs of the lunar surface taken by astronauts reveal fine lineaments that are merely centimetres apart. Taken together, all these linear features and their underlying fractures may be referred to as the lunar grid system. Prevalent on both the near and far sides of the Moon, the grid system is of fundamental importance in connexion with the origin and development of the Moon itself and of its surface. With an understanding of the grid system, one can move on to understand the origins of the smaller craters and the evolution of the larger craters and maria.

Soon after I began lunar research in a department of astronomy, I realised that disciplines other than astronomy would also be needed if I were to make sound progress in my understanding of the various lunar features. I decided to promote an interdisciplinary approach by drawing together specialist scientists in order to supplement my own training and to work together on the outstanding problems of the lunar surface. The scientific results drawn from the various lunar spacecraft investigations and, in particular, from the Apollo missions to the Moon have added importantly to the development of my ideas about the origins of the Moon's surface features. These developments, together with the inputs from my interdisciplinary teams, have enabled me to demonstrate that the Moon sports craters of widely different geneses; and that many individual craters have had complex developments. In addition to the craters, I have considered the origins of other important and, I hope, interesting features in the evolutionary story of the lunar surface. In preparing this monologue, I have been able to explain, consolidate, revise and build on my own, and my teams', published texts, as well as to present my recent thoughts on the subject.

In seeking a way forward, I have let our detailed observations of the lunar surface speak. On more than one occasion, these observations have given me cause to reject a conventional view. The text closes with a short section on some problems that might be tackled following a manned return to the Moon.

Many of the papers from which I draw succour were published in professional journals and specialised documents that are not easily accessible, and some might be rather technical to be followed by the non-scientist. Hoping to overcome at least some of these obstacles, I have eliminated nearly all mathematics from my story without, I think, much loss of accuracy; and I have referred quite frequently to textual illustrations in the form of photographs and diagrams. In the case of the Lunar Orbiter imagery, photo-strips, joined to complete each mosaic, show up frequently as parallel bands. The reader may wish to access the imagery of more lunar features by searching the relevant web sites of NASA, ESA, Roscosmos, CNSA, CSA and JAXA. (For abbreviations, please consult the Glossary.)

Based partly on my University courses in lunar geology (London) and in planetary science (Lancaster), this concise, up-to-date account of at least a part of the development of the Moon's surface will be useful to both undergraduate and research students and their tutors; but I hope that it will also be read and enjoyed by the professional scientist who has spent little time studying the Moon, by all those who plan to facilitate a return to our satellite, by the amateur astronomer and even by the dedicated layman with a keen interest in lunar science.

–Gilbert Fielder, 2021

Acknowledgements

The research described in this book was sponsored by Imperial Chemical Industries, the Department of Scientific and Industrial Research, the Science Research Council and the Natural Environment Research Council and was facilitated through the Universities of Manchester, London, Arizona and Lancaster. I am particularly grateful to C. W. Allen, S. E. Hollingworth and M. Wells for their sustained support; to Sir Edward Bullard and Sir Bernard Lovell for suggesting critical pathways for me to follow; to K. Runcorn for many fruitful discussions; and to A. Dollfus for the collaboration between our research groups.

I thank all the members of my successive research teams for their individual impacts on our progress in solving lunar issues. Special thanks go to L. Wilson, R. Fryer, J. Guest, H. Pinkerton, G. Hulme, S. Sparks, J. Whitford Stark and my wife, Jane, for their devotion to the research. Prof. Wilson critically read the draft manuscript and I incorporated his several useful improvements.

Essential photographic and map materials were provided gratuitously through the courtesies of G. Kuiper (University of Arizona: Lunar Photographic Atlases and support material for Ranger studies); J. Vette (World Data Center A for Rockets and Satellites: invaluable, large format Lunar Orbiter photographs and support material); and R. Carder (U.S.A.F. Aeronautical Chart and Information Center: regular mailings of the useful A.C.I.C. charts of the Moon). Throughout my account, I have been able to use the excellent photographs generated from NASA's many missions to the Moon. These photographs have formed a vital contribution to my analysis; and NASA's practice of making imagery accessible, by placing it in the public domain, is commendable and of definite assistance to researchers.

Rock samples returned from the Moon were loaned by NASA (solids) and lunar surface fines were presented by the Russian Academy of Sciences.

I thank R. Sutton, C. Edwards, O. Edwards and S. Bennett for teaching me most of what I know about digital processing; and my Editors, R. Davies and K. Barr, for their very competent guidance.

Without the inclusion of a large number of lunar photographs, I could not have clearly explained my research methods and results to the general reader. Strenuous attempts to achieve all copyright permissions have been made, but, if any illustrations have escaped the correct credit, I would ask any interested party to please contact my publisher.

G.F.

Author Bio

Dr. Gilbert Fielder is Reader Emeritus at Lancaster University, United Kingdom. He performed extended teaching at Lancaster University on Planetary Science and introduced a new degree course on Remote Sensing. Prior to this, he was Principal Investigator in NASA's Heat Capacity Mapping Programme, while continuing to head the Lunar and Planetary Unit at Lancaster until retirement. Dr. Fielder has authored several books, and presented many BBC and ITA television news programmes, as well as popular programmes with Sir Patrick Moore (on the BBC's "The Sky at Night") and, on the occasion of the first landing of astronauts on the Moon, with David Frost as Chairman in a special programme.

FIGURE 0.1   The Author [Katie Edwards]

Preparatory Studies

1

At any time of the year, the full Moon (Fig. 1.1) is surely an alluring sight. Out for an evening's walk with my father, when I was eight years old, I remember looking hard at the full Moon and asking about the nature of the dark patches on the Moon. In response to the question, my father surprised me by saying that he didn't really know what composed the dark patches. Then he thought that they were probably tonal changes of the rocks. Not satisfied with that answer, I decided, there and then, that I would work towards finding the answer. lt was 1940. A definitive answer to that question would be provided some 29 years later when Neil Armstrong and Buzz Aldrin would climb cautiously down the ladder of their lunar module (Fig. 1.2) and drop from the lowest step onto one of those dark patches, Mare Tranquillitatis.

In 1952, my brother presented me with a copy[2] of R. Baldwin's "The Face of the Moon" - a leading thesis on the impact origin of the lunar craters. A few years later I was involved in a lengthy correspondence with Baldwin, in which I questioned some of his arguments. With a London science degree behind me in 1954, I felt that I had the beginnings of a general foundation that would prove useful in my studies of the Moon. Impatient to learn about the Moon during these years of background study, I used my spare time to read all the lunar literature that I could get my hands on. H. Urey's book[1] "The Planets" was an early acquisition that interested me very much. Little did I know, then, that, in 1957, I would be facing Urey (Fig. 1.3) as the external examiner of my doctoral thesis, "Studies in Lunar Topography".

Using a set of 18 photographs of the Moon taken at the Lick Observatory, California, I was able to mosaic the prints and mount the finished photographic map, presenting a lunar diameter of about 1 metre, on rigid wooden boards. The photographs were accompanied by annotated diagrams that could be used to identify the most important named lunar features. This resulted in a useful photographic rendering of the near side of the Moon and, used along with the lunar literature, it acted as an excellent reference map[*].

By this means, and by the occasional use of a 3-inch refractor, I soon grew to learn about the locations and characteristics of many named lunar craters and other surface features. lt also became clear to me that the repeated use of a telescope used over many lunations and, importantly, under different conditions of illumination of the lunar surface (shortening shadows during local lunar sunrise and lengthening shadows

DOI: 10.1201/9781003181279-1

FIGURE 1.1 This photograph of the near side of the Moon clearly shows Mare Imbrium (diameter 1123 km, occupying the top-left portion of the northern latitudes) and, near the bottom, the bright ray crater Tycho (diameter 102 km) with its dark halo. In the far north, the dark-floored crater Plato (109 km) is easy to find. These, and other, features may be located on one of the maps referenced in section 1. [NASA]

during sunset over the same area) was vital in order to provide the data for a sound understanding of the forms of lunar features.

It seemed to me that professional astronomers and geologists rarely spent much time studying lunar topography. In fact, dedicated amateur lunar observers whom I encountered in the 1950s frequently had more knowledge about the niceties of the lunar surface features than did the professionals. In particular, the well-known amateur astronomer Patrick Moore (later, Sir Patrick) sent me a copy of his early book[5] "Guide to the Moon" which, through his telescopic observations of the Moon, highlighted some interesting questions for lunar students to mull over. Of course, with the advent of many excellent lunar photographs later in the space age, the position for the lunar researcher was eased. Nevertheless, a photograph relates to one particular instant; and the lunar student who relies on a few photographs as a source of information captures only part of the total possible range of data about the area under study. My access to a sizable telescope had to wait until the mid-1950s. In the meantime, I collected as many photographs as possible of different parts of the Moon.

Yet getting acquainted with selenography (the geography of the Moon) by whatever means was, I realised, an essential but not a sufficient prerequisite to use

FIGURE 1.2 E. Aldrin descending from the Apollo 11 Lunar Module to work on the lunar surface with N. Armstrong, who took this photograph. [NASA]

when attempting to solve the problems surrounding the nature and origin of the lunar surface features. For that, one certainly needed a knowledge of astronomy; but the Moon was a rocky object and the student of the Moon also required a knowledge of geology. At the time, I knew of no professional astronomers who had a geological training. Nor did I know of any geologists who had more than a passing interest in astronomy. I think that this situation was the principal cause of the different views proffered, respectively, by astronomers and geologists on the origin of the craters. It was time, I thought, for a new approach to lunar studies.

In a move to formalise my approach to the Moon, I applied to study for a post-graduate degree course in astronomy at the University of Manchester. The start date

FIGURE 1.3 In 1934, H. Urey was awarded the Nobel Prize in recognition of his discovery, in 1931, of deuterium. He became a keen lunar student, prolific in his publications in many of which, unlike the present author, he argued for a rigid Moon. [Lunar and Planetary Institute, Houston, TX., U.S.A.]

was September 1954 and, until then, I spent much of the summer reading further books and articles on general astronomy as well as on specifically lunar astronomy. Because I believed that many of the Moon's secrets would be concealed in its geology, I also started my geological studies by working through the mammoth volumes[4] on selenology (lunar geology) by the U.S.A. geologist J. E. Spurr. His volumes were published over the period 1945–1949 and, at that time, Spurr had no access to lunar rock specimens. Indeed, he concentrated on the structural geology that could be deduced using the best photographs that were available to him, obtaining them from the Mount Wilson, Lick and Yerkes Observatories.

With my photographic map standing next to me, I could find each of the lunar surface features that Spurr himself had identified using T. G. Elger's "Map of the Moon". Having recourse to my photomap also meant that I was able to study the regional setting of each feature. It was a tedious procedure but I considered it important to try to relate Spurr's sketches to the corresponding features on the photographs. Could I use my map to confirm all the details that he described in his texts? Not in every instance, partly because his sketches were rather poor; but I regarded his books as a rich source of ideas. In particular, I considered many of Spurr's observations of local and regional lunar structure across the near side of the Moon (the side we can see from the Earth) to be springboards to the interpretation of lunar processes that no lunar student could afford to ignore – not least in a search for information about the origin of the craters.

At that time I had considered most of the large lunar craters to be of impact origin. Around that time, I experimented with the modelling of impact craters using powders, seen as materials of very low cohesive strength, because I reasoned with others that meteoroids striking the Moon at high velocity might well behave like fluids. By preparing cement powders of different colours and placing them in layers on a board of area about 4 square feet and then dropping a dessertspoonful of powder from a height of a few feet above the centre of the board, I generated craters that I could solidify by misting with water and then allowing to set. The solid models could be sliced to reveal informative cross-sections. It was readily shown that the deepest layer on the board, before the impact, appeared as the uppermost layer forming the walls of a crater, after the impact. This inversion of the stratigraphy had been observed in field examples of terrestrial impact craters. Central peaks were produced when the total thickness of all the layers of powder was small (hard substratum); for greater thicknesses, craters without central peaks were produced.

NOTE

* For ease of reference, the reader might find it helpful to consult one of the Atlases listed at the end of this book as numbers 3, 73 and 74. Readers who use a small telescope will find references 73 and 74 advantageous.

Studies at Manchester and the Pic du Midi

2

By September 1954, I was installed in an attic of the Schuster Building of the Victoria University of Manchester. I spent the first months studying general astronomy as well as reading literature on the Solar System and, in particular, on the Moon. This learning process was supplemented by my attending lectures and colloquia on stellar and planetary physics, modern atomic physics, numerical analysis and computing (using the Ferranti Mark 2 computer). For informal discussion, staff coffee and tea times, organised by the Secretaries of the Physics and Astronomy Departments, proved to be profitable forums. They were held in a small room used, in the early twentieth century, by E. Rutherford for his groundbreaking experiments on the structure of the atom.

Over the next few years I made full use of two wonderful libraries: the Christie Library of the University and the City's Central Library. I researched the lunar literature covering the period 1800 to 1950 and noted that, regarding the more realistic theories of the origin of lunar craters, opinions were split roughly equally between the impact and volcanic theories. This dichotomy of opinion was striking and I thought that it deserved an explanation. What was needed, to judge the matter properly, was many more pertinent observations of the Moon and a sound science base involving a knowledge not only of physics and astronomy but, also, of certain other subjects. Of those, I was now confident that geology was to be ranked as of high importance.

As a Manchester University research student I was well placed to access selected undergraduate lectures given by the staff of four excellent Departments: astronomy, radioastronomy, physics, and geology. From the lofty heights of the Schuster building (my astronomy base) I could look down on an adjacent building to see a large table around which many geologists were taking tea or coffee, twice every working day, in an environment that seemed to be pervaded by amicable discussion. I was delighted when W. Deer, Head of the Department of Geology, agreed to be my joint PhD supervisor with Z. Kopal, who headed the Department of Astronomy. Starting to make good my deficiencies in geology, I studied[6] A. Holmes' "Principles of Physical Geology", for general background, and E. Anderson's "The Dynamics of Faulting", which[7] was to lead me into my own studies of rock fracturing and selenotectonics (the structure of the lunar rocks). I also attended Prof. Deer's course on volcanology. This learning process was supplemented by regular

DOI: 10.1201/9781003181279-2

discussions with the Manchester geologists (in particular, Drs. Howie, Nicholls and Zussman) who were remarkably tolerant of my questioning.

Seeking advice relating to impact cratering I visited the ICI Nobel Division at Stevenston, in 1955, to observe the formation of secondary craters in a sheet of lead when a copper-cased detonator had been placed centrally, in an upright position, on the lead and fired. The rows of secondary craters produced (Fig. 2.1) were aligned in strictly radial fashion. As we shall discover, the same relationship between crater and throwout does not apply to many of the lunar craters.

The next year found me at the Safety in Mines Research Establishment, on the Derbyshire moors near Buxton, where an SMRE scientist showed me how to prepare charges of blasting gelignite and detonate them at different depths in large volumes of materials that included a slurry and various granular substances. The explosions were recorded by a photographer who used a 15 mm film cine-camera. This allowed me to study the trajectoriess of ejected particles as functions of the depth of charge. The results (Fig. 2.2) helped me to understand the circumstances that led to high- and low-angle ejections of debris in application to the formation of the ray systems (Fig. 2.3) that are associated with some lunar craters.

My PhD topic centred on the construction of lunar land profiles through observations of the changing lengths of shadows cast by lunar mountains (and lesser eminences) during local lunar sunrise and sunset photo-sequences. In order to do this, I was able to modify a 35 mm film holder so that it could be used to take time-lapse (cine) photographs automatically, when bolted to the 60 cm Baillaud refractor (Fig. 2.4) that was sited at the high-altitude Pic-du-Midi Observatory in the French Pyrenees. At the time, "the Pic" was reputed to be one of the best observatories in the

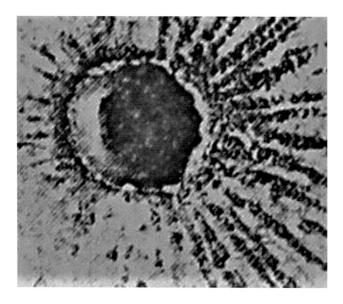

FIGURE 2.1   Crater chains radial to a crater produced by exploding a copper-cased detonator that was standing upright on a sheet of lead. [G. Fielder]

FIGURE 2.2 Experimental cratering using blasting gelignite placed in various media, showing ranges in the angles of projection of materials as a function of the depths of explosion centres. [G. Fielder]

world for lunar and planetary studies. The Head of Manchester University's Department of Radio Astronomy, B. Lovell, gave me permission to test my automatic equipment using an 18-inch reflector housed in its own small observatory at Jodrell Bank. For three years, starting in 1955, I was also able to use this optical telescope visually, to supplement my knowledge of lunar features on every available clear night.

Jodrell Bank, also known as the Nuffield Radio Astronomical Laboratories, was then in the news because of Professor (later, Sir Bernard) Lovell's protracted tussle for funds to meet the increasing costs of construction of his 250 ft (the diameter of the dish) radio telescope. Each time l visited Jodrell, I was able to note how the (then) largest steerable radio "dish" in the world was growing. The telescope had the potential to examine the physical state of small parts of the lunar surface; and I was pleased to have discussions with radio astronomers and attend some of their seminars. Transport for me between Manchester and Jodrell took the form of an old (even then) Ford 8 that belonged to the Physics Department. The car was equipped with transverse leaf springs and I knew just how fast to approach corners, on the way to Jodrell, without tipping the car over! Sometimes, I would be going in, through the gate at Jodrell, and Lovell would be leaving for the night. "You won't see so much tonight," he said, on one fairly cloudy occasion, "there's a lot of static coming in". He was right: the Moon only peeped through the clouds, that night. In my studies of lunar craters, Lovell strongly advised a statistical approach; and I was soon to embark on such a course.

Although the Pic site and telescope combination was excellent (weather permitting) for visual work on the Moon and planets, filming was more tricky. The focal length of the object glass (lens) was a huge 18 m and the nature of the secondary spectrum (where the different colours of light each came to a separate focus along the optic axis) meant that, in order to achieve a sharp focus on a photographic emulsion, much of the incoming light would have to be filtered out. On the other hand, the disc of the Moon's image at the prime focus measured 16 cm across; and this large image scale allowed me to conduct photography at the prime focus without the need for further

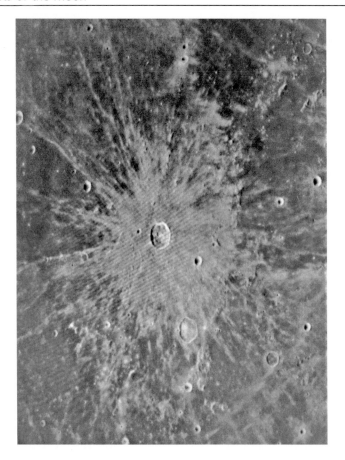

FIGURE 2.3 The rays of the lunar crater Kepler, 31 km in diameter. Kepler may be located in Fig. 1.1 to the west (left) of the bright ray crater Copernicus which, itself, is just south of Mare Imbrium. [From the Photographic Lunar Atlas, Plate E4c (W), in Gerard P. Kuiper. © (Ed.), The University of Chicago 1960, courtesy UC Press]

enlargement. The Moon offered plenty of light so filtering some of it out, although leading to long exposure times of ¾ sec which would potentially degrade image quality, would not matter too much given good "seeing" (stable air conditions).

Dr. Burg of Kodak Laboratories helpfully provided me with a number of 35 mm films, each film coated with a different emulsion that came with full description of its spectral sensitivity (how the film would respond to light of different wavelengths). After rigorous laboratory testing of these emulsions under different conditions of development and relating each development to the resulting grain size, which was relevant in seeking the best resolution of lunar surface features, I was able to select a few films for final testing using the Pic's 60 cm refractor.

Access to the Pic-du-Midi Observatory was via two téléphériques (cable-cars). The first-stage cable car could carry 15 people and was used by astronomers and by skiers from La Mongie, a settlement 15 miles up a mountain road from Bagnières-de-Bigorre,

FIGURE 2.4   The author with his photographic equipment at the prime focus of the 60cm refractor of the Pic-du-Midi Observatory. The film holder, which slides on the optical bench, can be seen to be fitted with a microscope and reflex system for focussing. [A. Batten]

Hautes Pyrénées. The second-stage cabin, used only by astronomers[*], could take up to 5 people; and the support cables spanned two, breathtaking valleys. The cabin climbed steeply across the second valley from the lowest point of the catenary, itself half a mile or so above the valley below, to reach the docking bay of the Observatory that had been constructed on the mountain top some 9,400 feet (3,000 m) above sea level.

On a good night, the Pic was well above the tops of any cumulus clouds, which effectively blanketed the warm air from the lower areas that had been heated by the Sun during the day. This tended to lead to stable atmospheric conditions. On such a night, the 60 cm refractor provided unparalleled viewing and photo-opportunities to reveal the surface details of the Moon. On the quite frequent poorer nights, when the atmosphere might have carried wind-blown particles, for example, the conditions were not suitable for good quality imaging by photography but, on such nights, I was often rewarded by observing the Moon visually. The eye has the advantage over traditional film photography in that the eye allows one to glimpse lunar surface detail in those instants when, for as little as 1/000th of a second, the image steadies.

In the case of my automated cine photography, sequential exposures of $^3/_4$ second were made at fixed intervals of 1 minute of time; so it was not possible to select the best instants at which to expose the film. But even long shadows, measured on the film, changed in length, between successive exposures, by considerably less than the size of the seeing disc (see Box 2.1). As a consequence, I was able to select the best negative from a sequence of 5 or so frames and, back in Manchester, measure the appropriate shadows on that negative.

BOX 2.1   SEEING DISC

Ideally, a point of light (such as a star) in the sky will reach the focal plane of a telescope also as a point of light. For a telescope on the Earth, however, the mobile atmosphere is of patchy density and transparency and can distort the incoming light in a number of ways, adding to the effects of the optical deficiencies of the telescope. The point of light can move around and/or expand in the focal plane to cover a small area referred to as the seeing disc. An extended object, such as part of the Moon, may be regarded as a composition of a large number of points of light.

With this amount of preparation, I felt that I was ready to plunge into productive lunar work and discover some of the secrets of the Moon.

NOTE

* A completely new system now enables members of the public to visit the observatories.

Wrinkle Ridges

3

In applying this method of lunar surface profiling to the determination of the nature of certain features, I first turned my attention to wrinkle ridges, also commonly referred to as mare ridges; but that term is not a good alternative to the term wrinkle ridges: (see Glossary). In his book "The Face of the Moon", Chicago 1949, R. Baldwin argued[2] that lavas had flowed from Mare Imbrium, through the gap (Fig. 3.1) between the Caucasus and Apennine Mountains, to flood Mare Serenitatis.

FIGURE 3.1 Sunrise shadows in retreat across a wrinkle ridge that crosses the gap between the Caucasus (centre to upper R) and the Apennines (lower L). The two shadowed craters are in Mare Imbrium, while part of Mare Serenitatis is seen to the lower R. [G.Fielder, Pic-du-Midi, 60 cm refractor. Courtesy J. Rosch]

DOI: 10.1201/9781003181279-3

I hesitated to accept this interpretation because my visual impressions of the wrinkle ridges in Mare Imbrium – and specifically the one that was near to the Caucasus-Apennine gap was that, rather than their being the fronts of lava flows, they were built by the extrusion of lavas. Dealing with the matter in more quantitative fashion, my measurements[8] of shadows that, during sunrise, retreated across the 20 km wide wrinkle ridge in question led me to the conclusion that the general level of the land bordering each side of the ridge was about the same. I estimated that level to be 250 ± 116 m lower than the top of the ridge. This result shows that this wrinkle ridge is not the front of a frozen lava flow: the latter would form a step down, rather than a step up followed by an equal step down.

Some authors have considered wrinkle ridges to be compression features but this is not borne out by the evidence. In 1959, G. Kuiper[9] (Fig. 3.2) observed that several wrinkle ridges had cracked open along their crests and that, frequently, the cracks were filled with light-coloured rocks that resembled extrusive dykes. Noticing that these dyke-like outcrops took the form of linear elements or segments, T. Kiang and I measured the orientations of the segments that capped the wrinkle ridges in Mare Imbrium, along with the orientations of the major ridge lineaments around Mare Imbrium, and deduced[10] (Fig. 3.3) that the wrinkle ridges were associated with deep structural elements in the lunar crust. This result confirmed Kuiper's argument that the

FIGURE 3.2   G. P. Kuiper, outside the Lunar and Planetary Laboratory, Tucson. [G. Fielder]

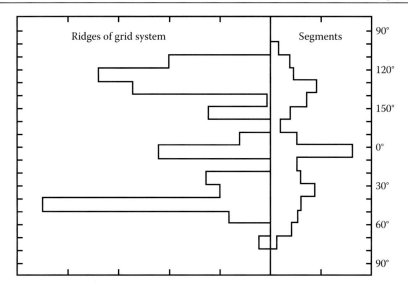

FIGURE 3.3 These back-to-back histograms will enable the reader to compare the trends of wrinkle-ridge segments with the regional trends of the grid system. On the vertical axis, 0° corresponds to the northerly direction. The angles pass through east to 180°. [G. Fielder and T. Kiang[10]]

wrinkle ridges were extrusion features. Before solidifying, most of these late lavas flowed for some 10 km to either side of the inferred extrusion vents and, in the process, built up the complex mare ridges. Clearly, the overall trend of such a ridge does not necessarily reveal its deep fracture origin. This has led to some false claims that the widespread lunar fracture system (which I shall detail later) is not in evidence in Mare Imbrium. Crucially, the evidence from our work is that the underlying fractures that delivered the lavas to form wrinkle ridges run in preferred directions (Fig. 3.3) – at angles of roughly 45° to meridians. The significance of that observation will be evident following further discussion.

The Straight Wall

4

In another application of the time-lapse photographic method, I examined the not very well-named Straight Wall (Fig. 4.1) which is, however, well-known to lunar observers because, at some 112 km long, it is an easily recognisable step in relatively level, uncluttered terrain. Those readers who are not familiar with the different kinds of geological fault may wish to consult Fig. 4.2. Complementary sets of strike-slip faults (Fig. 4.3) also commonly occur in planetary crusts.

The overall strike of the Straight Wall is always inclined to the plane of the Sun's path and, for a short time each lunar morning, this leads to eye-catching shadows (Fig. 4.4). Measuring these shadows on film that I exposed at the Pic-du-Midi led me to estimate the heights of points, distributed along the top of the Wall, above the terrain to the west of the Wall. (Fig. 4.5). Negatives of shorter shadows, provided by D. Alter, were also measured. Because the land to either side of the Wall is not flat, the heights deduced might be expected to depend on the lengths of the shadows used in the computations. Indeed, I found that short shadows were associated with height differences between the upper edge of the Wall and the ground below of about 300 m; whereas long shadows yielded differential heights of about 380 m. Commonly, errors in these results (Fig. 4.5) were found to be ±10% of the altitudes but were, occasionally, twice as large. The highest part of the Straight Wall, measured above the ground below, was found to be near to its centre, which might possibly have been lifted by 100 m or so above either end[11]. In reference to my sketch map (Fig. 4.6), the Straight Wall can be described[12] as "several short, small-curvature arcs, generally concave to the downthrown side. This is a well-known characteristic of faults and there can be no doubt that the Straight Wall is a selenological fault".

Of course, digital photography (used later in this account) has largely supplanted traditional photographic methods but lunar land profiles drawn from time-lapse studies using the methods described here are still useful: even a digital time-lapse method will encounter some of the difficulties that I have listed[11,83] in connexion with the estimation of the true lengths of lunar shadows. For example, solar penumbral effects and shadow tip effects that result from the roughness of the lunar terrain will persist.

DOI: 10.1201/9781003181279-4

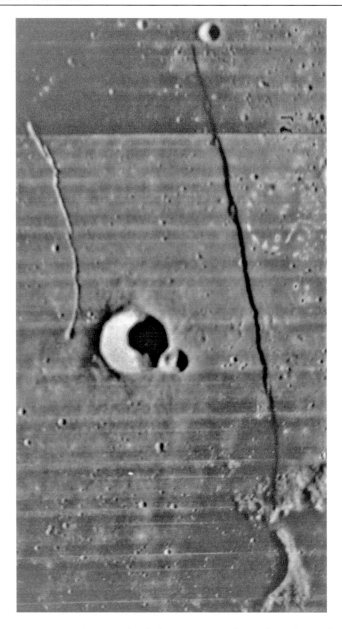

FIGURE 4.1 A morning photograph of the lunar Straight Wall casting a short shadow. Birt, the larger of the two craters to the W of the Wall has a diameter of 16 km. [Lunar Orbiter IV mosaic, NASA]

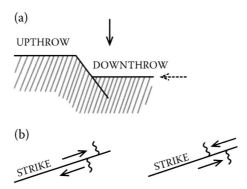

FIGURE 4.2   (a) Cross-section of an idealised dip-slip fault in a vertical plane. A dip-slip fault is produced when the vertical stress in a planetary crust is the greatest (solid arrow) and the stress that is directed at right angles to the strike (the trace of the fault as seen from above) is the least (broken arrow). (There is a third principal stress, intermediate in value between the other two, acting perpendicularly to the paper.) [G. Fielder]. (b) Plan of a right-lateral (dextral) strike-slip fault where the curly line represents a feature offset to the R when viewed across the strike. Also, plan of a left-lateral (sinistral) strike-slip fault in which the curly line represents a feature offset to the L when viewed across the strike. In these cases, the greatest crustal stress acts at an angle of less than 45° to the strike; and the country rock on one side of the strike moves, along the strike, relative to that on the other side: the least crustal stress acts at right angles to the greatest stress and a stress of intermediate value acts vertically, in each case. [G. Fielder]

In addition to the shadows method, I also used a recording microdensitometer[12] in an attempt to examine the slopes of the upthrown and downthrown portions of the degraded ring structure that is marked X in the sketch map (Fig. 4.6). The ring measures about 190 km in diameter and is bisected by the Straight Wall. I found that, whereas the downthrow near to the Wall was fairly level and comparatively smooth, the upthrow appeared to slope gently away from the highest (central) part of the Wall, towards the N, S and E. One possibility is that the floor of the ring X was slightly domed, prior to faulting, while, subsequent to the faulting, the downthrown block was covered, and levelled, by lavas. Faulting at Thebit α could be seen as extending the length of the feature in the southern direction (note the craters 1 to 4 in the sketch).

In plan, the face of the Straight Wall might measure about 2 km in width. In principle, the width and height of the face can be used to estimate a slope: I was able to evaluate it only between the wide limits of 10° and 40°. In any case, this slope relates to what we can observe - which could be scree, for example, rather than a part of the original fault face. The lineament F-G, shown in the sketch map, cuts across the Straight Wall and does not seem to offset it laterally. The lineament R-P does seem to

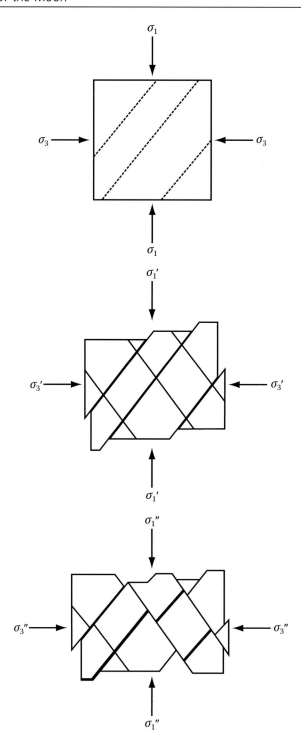

(caption on next page)

FIGURE 4.3 Complementary sets of strike-slip faults. In this idealised diagram, sigma 1 is the greatest principal stress and sigma 3 the least. Note that, as the stresses are relieved by faulting, the values of the stresses change. [G. Fielder]

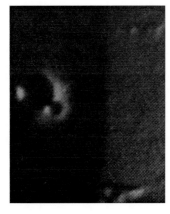

FIGURE 4.4 Long, early morning shadow cast by the Straight Wall. [G. Fielder, Pic-du-Midi, 60 cm refractor. Courtesy J. Rosch.]

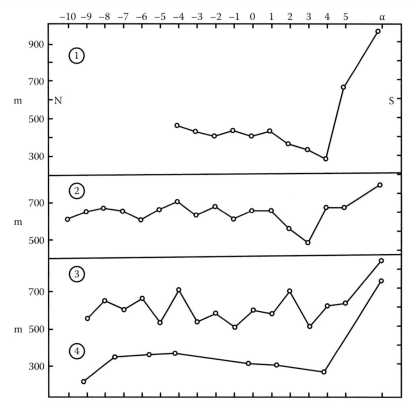

FIGURE 4.5 Computed relative altitudes along the upper edge of the Straight Wall. Plot 1 is from my measurements of long shadows, while Plot 2 is based on my short shadow photographs. Plot 3 is taken from a short shadow negative of D. Alter. Finally, visual estimates by J. Ashbrook of shadows of intermediate length were used to construct Plot 4. Taken together, the four plots show that the highest point is near to the centre of the Straight Wall around point –4. (Points 4 and 5 relate to the hills at the south end of the Wall proper and have been discarded in finding the highest point of the Wall.) [G. Fielder[11]]

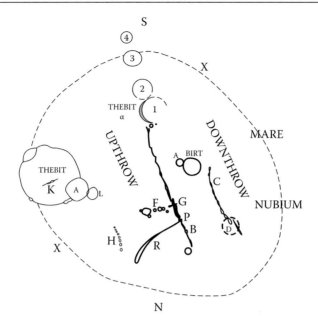

FIGURE 4.6   Sketch map of the Straight Wall and its immediate surroundings. [G. Fielder[12]]

offset the Wall but the strike-slip movement would be in a direction along R-P rather than along the Wall.

In fact, there are other probable lunar dip-slip faults that run in, or close to, a meridional direction. Together, they are indicative of local crustal pressures that are least in the E-W direction. Again, the significance of this observation will be developed later.

Thoughts on Mare Imbrium

5

In 1960, I moved from my Manchester base to the University of London Observatory (ULO) where I continued to study the Moon – first, as Imperial Chemical Industries Research Fellow for 3 years and then, for another 3 years, as Honorary Research Assistant supported be the Department of Scientific and Industrial Research. Although ULO was sited at Mill Hill, NW7, it was part of University College, London (UCL) so, once again, I was able to benefit by forging links with the geologists there, especially those with tectonic and volcanological specialities. For example, Professor M. Wells spent many hours with me, sharing his impeccable knowledge of the Scottish ring complexes. London University also provided easy access to other specialists and I soon found several helpful colleagues in Photogrammetry (UCL) and advanced tectonics (Imperial College).

The near side of the Moon seemed to me, and others, to be dominated by Mare Imbrium (Fig. 5.1) and its associated system of ridges and troughs that splayed out across the central parts of the Moon's face. The features had been discussed frequently, in the literature, particularly since 1893 when the geologist G.K. Gilbert published[13] his view that Mare Imbrium was the scar left after a major collision. He supposed that a deluge of material - solid, pasty and liquid (Fig. 5.2) – was ejected in all directions to form the lunar "furrows". One might expect the furrows (actually, fairly straight ridges and troughs which, for convenience, may all be referred to as lineaments) to be oriented roughly radially with respect to the explosion centre. For comparison, reference may be made to the radial patterns made by ejecta from an exploding detonator (see section 2.1). For the lineaments in the neighbourhood of the central parts of the Moon's near face, each lineament may be extended towards Mare Imbrium along a great circle (one following the curvature of the Moon); and these interpolations intersect to define a circular area[14], about 330 km in diameter, centred at 18° W, 31° N in Mare Imbrium (Fig. 5.3).

Rather than their being described as "radial" lineaments, the extrapolations shown in Fig. 5.3 are more correctly described as being "sub-radial" to the centre of that circular area.

A similar result had been found by Darney[15]. However, these authors did not have access to photographs of the far side of the Moon and so were unable to search very far for lineaments in the directions N and W of Mare Imbrium. I have been unable to find convincing evidence for many lineaments that are systematically sub-radial to Mare Imbrium in those directions; the most strongly developed lineaments (Fig. 5.4) of the

DOI: 10.1201/9781003181279-5

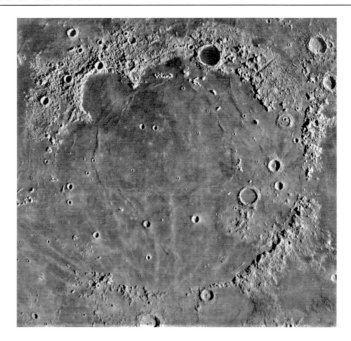

FIGURE 5.1   Mare Imbrium, traversed by the rays of Copernicus (93 km in diameter, near bottom). The mountains in the lower R are the Apennines, where structures that trend sub-radially with respect to Mare Imbrium may be noticed. To the north, the dark-floored crater Plato (109 km in diameter) and the larger, partially walled Sinus Iridum are conspicuous. Further north still the darker, foreshortened Mare Frigoris is visible. Notice the lineaments in the mountains immediately to the north of Sinus Iridum, where the most conspicuous lineaments run tangentially to the border of Mare Imbrium. [LRO, NASA]

FIGURE 5.2   Gross lineaments in the central areas of the Moon's near side will be found to run roughly parallel to each of the diagonals that join the corners of this image. [Adapted from E. Whitaker et al., Rectified Lunar Atlas, University of Arizona Press (1963), Plate 19b (Y)]

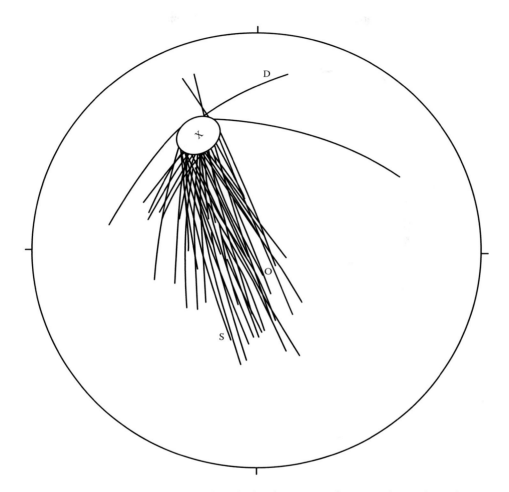

FIGURE 5.3 Lineaments associated with the formation of Mare Imbrium have been extrapolated along great circles to define the central area of Mare Imbrium shown here, measuring some 324 km across a diameter. Mare Imbrium itself has a diameter of about 1120km. [G. Fielder[14]]

Jura Mountains, north of Sinus Iridum, trend tangentially, rather than radially, to the centre just described.

Urey[1] had considered the possible asymmetry of the Mare Imbrium system of lineaments (judged only from near-side photographs) and had proposed that an object had collided obliquely with the Moon at a low velocity – the escape velocity of 2.4 km/sec. – in Sinus Iridum (Fig. 5.4) and had showered materials principally in the SE direction. This is in the direction of the mid-regions of the Moon's earthward-turned face. Under the pressures involved, "… the materials in the region of contact

FIGURE 5.4   Sinus Iridum is the arcuate structure on the SW border of Mare Imbrium and may be picked out towards the top of Fig. 5.1. Scrutiny of the mountains above and to the left of Sinus Iridum will reveal lineaments that run from top R to lower L, as well as some others that are sub-radial to Mare Imbrium. [Adapted from E. Whitaker et al., Rectified Lunar Atlas, University of Arizona Press (1963), Plate 5d (W)]

flowed like liquids and splashed to great distances … and even some of the un-differentiated planetary material was thrown into some ridges west of Copernicus. The body of the planetesimal melted and filled what is Mare Imbrium …."

These notions became embedded in the literature but the evidence that we now have militates against some of them. I have already shown that the sub-radial lineaments of Mare Imbrium trace back to a restricted area that lies in the central portion of Mare Imbrium: the centre of disturbance is certainly not in Sinus Iridum. The ridges (Fig 5.5) west, and south, of Copernicus, as well as those (Fig. 5.2) in the central parts of the Moon's earthward-facing hemisphere, could not all have been produced as splash deposits because, in many cases, the ridges identify with the walls of craters that appear to have suffered distortion. In fact, an examination of all the straight ridges of the lunar surface indicates that they frequently form linear portions of the walls of variously-sized, and variously aged, craters. Also, we now know that the lavas of Mare Imbrium that were sampled (and analysed after their return to Earth) in the Apollo 15 programme were not derived from an impact but came from deep locations in the lunar crust.

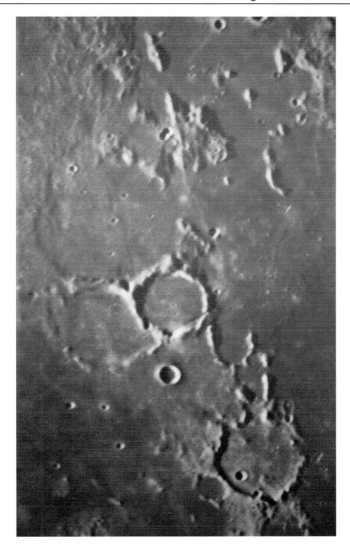

FIGURE 5.5 Here are some of the "splash deposits" of G. Gilbert; but notice that many such "deposits" form parts of the walls of distorted, or partially formed, craters. [From the Photographic Lunar Atlas, Plate D5b (W), in Gerard P. Kuiper. © (Eds.), The University of Chicago, 1960, courtesy UC Press]

My alternative theory of the origin of lineaments that fan out from Mare Imbrium over the central area of the Moon's nearside is bound up with the tectonics of the Moon. To follow this argument it will be necessary to look, first, at the natural stresses that are generated in the Moon.

The Apparent Acceleration of the Moon

6

Every time it completes one orbit of the Earth, the Moon rotates once about its axis. In other words, our natural satellite always presents nearly the same face to the Earth. In technical jargon, the Moon is locked to the Earth in synchronous rotation.

Noting the differing masses and distances of the Moon and the Sun from the Earth, calculations show that the Moon generates a tide-raising force on the Earth that exceeds that of the Sun. Because fluids and solids differ greatly in their physical properties and because the gravitational attraction which the Moon has on the Earth differs between the side of the Earth that is nearer to the Moon and the side of the Earth that is farther from the Moon, tides in the atmosphere, oceans and body of the Earth are raised at opposite sides of our planet (Fig. 6.1). The body tides are of smaller amplitude than that of the tides found in the oceans, but both influence the changing speed of rotation of the Earth; while atmospheric tides have a relatively minor effect on the Earth's rotation.

The Earth–Moon system is not isolated in space so, strictly, it is not a system that wholly conserves angular momentum: the Sun and nearby planets have a role to play in the gravitational effects that are observed in both bodies. As a result of the gravitational attractions of other Solar System planets on the Earth, its orbit around the Sun is slowly

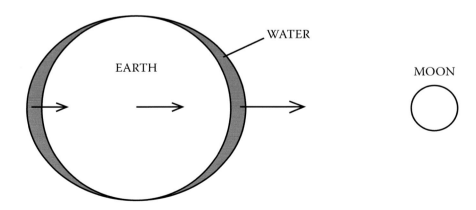

(caption on next page)

DOI: 10.1201/9781003181279-6

FIGURE 6.1   Schematic diagram of tides raised on the Earth. Newton's Law of Gravitation states that the gravitational force between two bodies is attractive and inversely proportional to the square of the distance between them. From this fundamental law it may be shown that the actual tide-raising force is proportional to the inverse cube of the distance between the two bodies. The centre of mass of the Earth–Moon system is a point on the line joining the centres of the Earth and Moon and is located at a (variable) distance beneath the Earth's surface. The centres of both the Earth and the Moon revolve in elliptical orbits around this centre of mass. For simplicity, consider a rigid Earth made up of concentric, spherical shells each of uniform composition. It is easy to prove that, at any point external to this model, the gravitational attraction of the whole sphere of the Earth is the same as if all the mass were concentrated at the centre of the Earth. Hence, the gravitational force with which the Moon attracts the Earth can be regarded as shifting the centre of the Earth by a small distance towards their centre of mass. Now introduce a thin layer of water to the whole surface of this idealised Earth. The water can be considered to have little internal strength. A unit mass in the water that is the closest to the Moon will be attracted (longest arrow in figure) by the Moon more than a unit mass at the central point that represents the Earth. Likewise, this mass will be attracted more by the Moon than a unit mass in the water that is farthest from the Moon: this water will be left behind (see shortest arrow in figure). As a consequence, water tides will be raised on both sides of the Earth. Allowing for the motion of the Moon in its orbit around the centre of mass of the Earth-Moon system (but not for the inclination of its orbit to the equator), at a fixed location on an Earth rotating as the real Earth does, such a simple model would be expected to lead to two high tides separated by a period of about 12 hrs 25 mins. The complete cycle of two high, and two low, tides would be expected to take twice as long. This simplified explanation of the water tides takes no regard of the fact that the Earth is neither rigid nor spherical (reference may be made to Fig. 12.8). Neither is each shell of the globe of uniform composition. And, in a world of variously shaped and disposed land masses, the real oceans do not behave like the unfettered water layer envisaged here. Furthermore, in the case of the real Earth-Moon system, the plane of the Moon's elliptical orbit is generally inclined to the plane of the Earth's equator (see Fig. 7.1). As in the foregoing, simplified case, and ignoring the relatively small body tides raised in the Earth, the Moon attracts the ocean waters and would tend to form a liquid, spheroidal shell encapsulating the Earth if its oblate spheroidal surface were smooth. The longest axis of this psuedo-spheroidal shell, in line with the Moon, is always oriented differently from the Earth's axis of rotation. Hence, a point at a given latitude on the Earth's rotating surface would, in general, experience two high tides a day, as found before; but, now, it is seen that the heights of these tides would, in general, differ. However, the heights of high tides at a given place would tend to equalise as the plane of the Moon's orbit approached the Earth's equatorial plane. In practice, each high tide is observed to lag the point on the Earth's surface that lies under the Moon. The time lag, resulting from the presence of land masses, varies from place to place. The Sun also raises tides on the Earth but they are not as high as those raised by the Moon. Spring tides are produced when the Moon and Sun are jointly attracting the Earth (in the same direction or in the opposed direction). Especially high tides occur when, at the same time as a Spring tide, the Moon is at the closest point in its orbit to the Earth. Neap tides occur when the Moon and Sun are attracting the Earth in two directions at right angles. Because of the constraints discussed above, some places experience only one, others more than two, tides per day. [G. Fielder]

becoming less eccentric (that is, closer to a circle). This reduces the average strength of the Sun's perturbation of the Moon and, to an observer who bases time on the Earth's rotation, that results in an apparent acceleration of the Moon in its orbit. Yet this process accounts for only about half of the Moon's apparent acceleration.

The Slowing Rotation of the Earth

7

Another source of the apparent orbital acceleration of the Moon is found in tidal friction. Despite the fact that the plane of the Earth's equator is inclined by about 23° to the ecliptic (the plane of the Earth's orbit) and the plane of the Moon's orbit is inclined by about 5° to the ecliptic (Fig. 7.1) the friction generated by water tides, and by body tides, is acting to slow the Earth's rotation about its axis by a measurable extent.

Because the Earth does not rotate at a rate that is constant, scientists have turned to the use of atomic clocks, over a manageable (short) interval of time, to study how that rate is changing. They calculate that the duration of the day is increasing by 0.002 seconds per century: these studies confirm that the Earth is slowing down in its rotation. The question is, for how long has this rate of slowing down been in operation?

The length of day in past epochs has been studied by palaeontologists who have examined the finely ridged growth lines on the surfaces of certain, well-preserved coral epitheca (the calcium carbonate that forms the outer covering, as well as inner partitions, of a coral). It has been shown that the rate at which corals acquire calcium carbonate is greater by day than at night, so the growth lines are thought to be indicative of daily growth. Coarser growth increments are thought to be formed at annual intervals. Because of the crudity of the observations, it is not surprising that there are wide variations in the results. Selected fossils from a few hundred millions of years ago indicate that the number of days per year has decreased since that period: qualitatively, the palaeontological data support the theory that the Earth's axial rotation has been slowing for as long as a few hundred million years.

Other processes might also be acting to change the motion of the Moon. For example, Urey proposed[1] that any iron that was still in the Earth's mantle might be sinking as part of a differentiation process that produced the core and that is now transferring mass to the core; whereas Runcorn (in Marsden & Cameron[16]) considered the possible separation of the Earth's materials of differing density to be caused by slow convection within the Earth. Taking into account the compressibility of rocks, he found that the change of the Earth's moment of inertia about the rotation axis, that would accompany the differentiation process, would shorten the length of day by about 3 hours over a period of

DOI: 10.1201/9781003181279-7

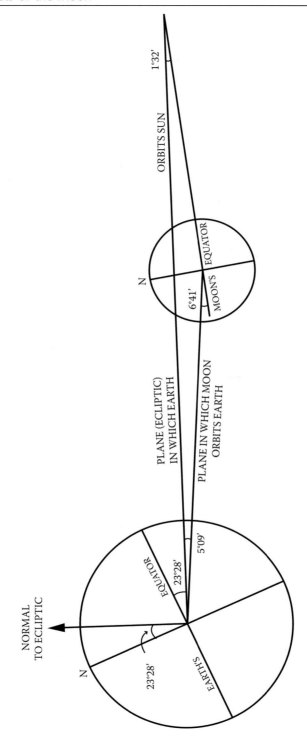

FIGURE 7.1 Schematic diagram, not to scale, showing the Earth and Moon and the present relationships between their orbital parameters. [G. Fielder]

a billion years. That is equivalent to a shortening of 0.001 second per century; and would correspond to a small acceleration, rather than a retardation, in the rotation of the Earth.

Yet again, climate change is currently causing some of the ice cover of Antarctica and Greenland to melt. Reducing the ice loads on these continents will lead to isostatic adjustments (in this case, their upward recovery) and possible lateral flow in the upper mantle; and ocean levels will increase, potentially changing the moment of inertia of the planet about its polar axis. At times in the past, these processes could well have been more important than they are now.

Even taking these presently smaller effects on the rotation rate of the Earth into account, it is evident that, when combined with the traditional effects on the Moon's orbital motion, the net effect preserves the Moon's secular acceleration in recent times.

The Receding Moon

8

Diverted by irregular continental coastlines, the oceanic tides of the Earth will generate friction – particularly across continental shelves and in shallow seas elsewhere. On another front, body friction will probably develop in the upper shells of the Earth's mantle and possibly also between the grains of fractured crustal rocks. Even the elasticity of the Earth will, over the years, be subject to change. It is easy to appreciate that these are complex processes and that the overall effects of tidal friction are likely to vary with time. More work needs to be done on this problem but, on balance, part of the probable net loss of rotational energy of the Earth is transferred to the Moon which, itself, gains potential energy and spirals away from the Earth. Consequently, by reference to the stellar background, the Moon is slowing down in its orbit around the Earth. Confusingly, the Moon appears to speed up with respect to a time-scale that is based on the Earth's rotation. The actual rate of the Moon's recession from the Earth is, presently, some 3.8 cm per year.

As we have seen, this rate might vary over the geological time scale. Therefore, it is probably unsafe to use it to calculate meaningful distances between the Earth and Moon in the distant past or in the far future. However, it is certainly safe to say that there are strong indications from the astronomical and geophysical theories that the Moon has been closer to the Earth, at least in the recent past.

DOI: 10.1201/9781003181279-8

Distorted Craters

9

A quite different method may now be employed to investigate the past proximity of the Moon to the Earth. It involves the prominent tectonic pattern that is exposed on the lunar surface. The pattern can be found in the vicinity of large craters (Fig. 9.1) but many more examples will follow. This pattern is predominantly of linear ridges, troughs and crater-chains – all of which may be grouped as lineaments, particularly since each linear feature may well be fracture-controlled. The pattern is widespread across the Moon and has been called the lunar grid system[4].

If reference is made to the Ariadaeus-Hyginus region (Fig. 9.2) of the Moon, it is easy to see that many craters in the area are far from circular. The longest axes of the distorted craters run in the direction of strongly developed, and ubiquitous, lineaments. There are two or three families of ridge-lineaments present in the area, each running in a different direction. If the lineaments that are specifically sub-radial to Mare Imbrium are removed from the picture, two other lineament families, that are of more general extent, remain. I shall label the more prominent set of lineaments, that has a south-easterly trend in this area and as it crosses the equator, "system A", and the other set, that trends south-westerly and intersects "system A" roughly at right angles, "system B".

I used the criteria other than the consideration of the degree of distortion of a crater to class it as either young or old. All craters in the area covered by a plate of the Photographic Lunar Atlas[85] that represents the Ariadaeus-Hyginus region can be approximated by ellipses. Measurements of the longer and shorter axes of each crater then led me to find that the mean percentage distortions of the craters were greater for the older craters than for the younger ones[17]. This showed that the crustal stresses that distorted the craters decreased in magnitude as time elapsed. At the time, I had thought that thrust faulting, acting in the direction of a crater's shortest axis, was the driving force that produced these distortions. A hint that that theory was wrong was provided by a simple laboratory experiment.

After preparing layers of modelling clay mounted on a metal mesh in a horizontal plane, I imprinted 7 cm diameter rings on the surface of the clay and then sheared the mesh either uniformly or along a specific plane and found[18] that the rings came remarkably close (Figs. 9.3 and 9.4) to matching the deformational characteristics of the distorted lunar craters, some of which are shown in Fig. 9.2. (In the absence of dimensional scaling, these experiments were of qualitative value only; but they hinted that the lunar shearing in the area of study was, principally, right-lateral.)

DOI: 10.1201/9781003181279-9

FIGURE 9.1 Lineaments on the far side of the Moon intersecting orthogonally immediately to the E of the 185 km diameter crater Tsiolkovski. [Apollo 15, NASA]

A further analysis of crater distortions, this time in the nearby Hipparchus region (see Fig. 5.2) showed that, again, the craters there had their longest axes most frequently lying parallel to system A lineaments. This time, my co-author C. Jordan and I allotted craters to one of three age groups, based on the following criteria: overlapping of craters; sharpness of floor and wall detail; height of wall for a given size; and the degree of "smoothing" of a crater's walls by erosion. And, again, the mean percentage distortions of the craters generally increased with crater age[19]. We also showed that the stresses that produced systems A and B must have acted together over the period during which all the distorted craters were formed. The results of our analyses of these two areas are, I think, significant. They mean that the most conspicuous fan of lineaments that is associated with Mare Imbrium reached its present state of development through active, probably strike-slip, faulting over a long period of time. So the sub-radial lineaments in question could not have been produced as a single incident throwout from an impact site.

Both the regions just considered are located in the central parts of the Earthward-turned hemisphere of the Moon. This is just the part of the (synchronous) Moon where

FIGURE 9.2 The Ariadaeus-Hyginus region of the Moon showing distorted craters. The Hyginus crater-rille is to the left, the Ariadaeus normal rille to the right. [From the Photographic Lunar Atlas, Plate C4b (W), in Gerard P. Kuiper. © (Eds.), The University of Chicago, 1960, courtesy UC Press]

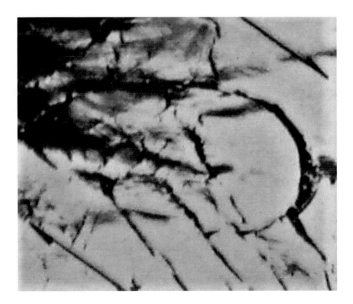

FIGURE 9.3 A laboratory model of a ring, impressed in clay and originally circular, after being subjected to uniform, right lateral shearing. [G. Fielder]

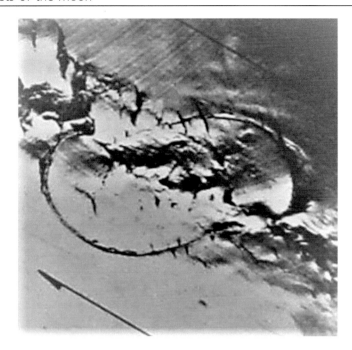

FIGURE 9.4   A laboratory model after a ring impressed in clay has been sheared along a specific plane. [G. Fielder]

tidal stressing is (and has been) maximised. Transmitting seismometers were set up on the Moon during the Apollo 11, 12, 14, 15 and 16 missions and led to the discovery of weak lunar seismic activity. Graphic proof of the Earth's stressing of the Moon was provided when the seismometers recorded moonquakes that repeated monthly, particularly around the time of perigee (the point, in the Moon's orbit, that is closest to the Earth). System A lineaments are better developed than those of system B, in the central regions of the near side, because the stressing caused by the formation of Mare Imbrium added to the stressing caused by the Earth. This combined, protracted stressing evidently led to the shaping of the distorted craters.

The Lunar Grid System

10

In an early discussion[14] of the grid system lineaments, I attempted to map the lunar lineaments on the near side of the Moon. In the process, I found that reasonable positional accuracy could be achieved only in the central one-third of the near-side hemisphere. For this mapping, I used Part 1 of the Orthographic Atlas of the Moon[20], compiled by Arthur, Kuiper and Whitaker, to read off the coordinates of each end of a line that represented the mean direction of a set of lineaments shown on parts of each plate. At the time, there was no atlas that covered the far side of the Moon. (The Russian Luna 3 had acquired very low-resolution images of the lunar far side in 1959.) My mapping resulted in a chart of systems A and B (Fig. 10.1). Analysis of the grid[14] showed that the lunar grid system was initiated as joints and fractures, some of which evolved to faults, all created by stresses in the rocks. The stresses must have been relatively uniform in both magnitude and direction because the grid pattern was maintained over large distances. I reasoned that both the Earth's attraction and the rotation of the Moon had influenced the orientations of the underlying fractures and, hence, of the subsequent linear ridges arising from the fractures, possibly by extrusion of lavas.

Some of the system A lineaments arose in right-lateral shear faults (Fig. 10.2). Some of the system B lineaments might be expected to follow left-lateral movements but are harder to find and document. The stresses caused by the formation of Mare Imbrium might be involved in an explanation of this difference, although there seems to be a 20 km left-lateral displacement of the wall of Regiomantanus (Fig. 10.3) along a probable fracture indicated by the largest crater-chain in Deslandres. Although theory would allow both right and left strike-slip faults to develop from the predicted System A and B fractures, the extrusion of lavas from a fracture could very easily obscure the evidence for strike-slip motions. Examples of lunar strike-slip faults have been listed in my book Lunar Geology[21], pages 106–108. In any such joint, or fracture, system, at least two principal sets of lineaments (systems A and B) would have been generated simultaneously. Interestingly, the seismometer records of a deep (800 km) focus moonquake that repeats monthly show a distinct "H" phase in the horizontal recordings[22], suggesting that a shearing mechanism is in operation even now.

As they cross the Moon's equator, the systems A and B intersect each other at angles spread around 90°. A 90° dihedral angle (the angle between two joint or fracture

DOI: 10.1201/9781003181279-10

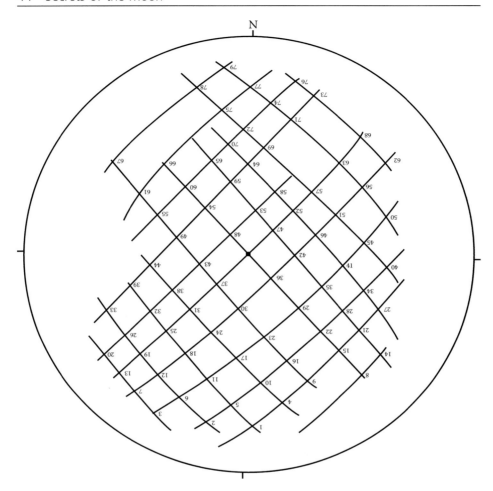

FIGURE 10.1 Orthographic chart of averaged directions of the grid systems A (running top L to bottom R) and B (running top R to bottom L). [G. Fielder]

planes where they intersect the surface) suggests that the lunar materials possessed only small angles of internal friction (see Fig. 10.4). These observations promote the idea that the underlying fractures that fashioned the grid system penetrated quite deeply into the Moon's crust, where the temperatures might have been higher than in the upper parts of the crust.

Not everyone would be convinced by a theory based on my quite restricted observations of the central one-third of the Moon's earthward- pointing face. I myself

FIGURE 10.2 The walls of Capella (42km diameter, with prominent central peak) and Gaudibert (29km diameter) showing right lateral offsets as the result of a long fault (running top L to bottom R). [From the Photographic Lunar Atlas, Plate B5e (W). Edited by Gerard P. Kuiper. © The University of Chicago 1960, courtesy UC Press]

was anxiously waiting to extend the work to the lunar far-side, as well as to the whole of the near-side. So when, in 1967, high-quality photo-coverage of, essentially, the whole Moon was processed on-board the NASA/Boeing Lunar Orbiter spacecraft, and transmitted to Earth, I could at last be certain that the grid system (Fig. 10.5) was a feature of the entire surface of the Moon – and not just of that part of the Moon facing the Earth.

In 1970, the nucleus of my lunar research group, then housed in a specially built Lunar Laboratory as an extension of the University of London Observatory, was offered more space at Lancaster University. There, I established the Lunar and Planetary Unit under the sponsorship of the Natural Environment Research Council and the

FIGURE 10.3   Left-lateral fault offsetting the wall of Regiomontanus (108 km diameter) as the result of a fault that is probably indicated again by the crater chain (at lower L) in Deslandres. [From the Photographic Lunar Atlas, Plate C6d (P). G. Kuiper. (Ed.), © The University of Chicago 1960, courtesy UC Press]

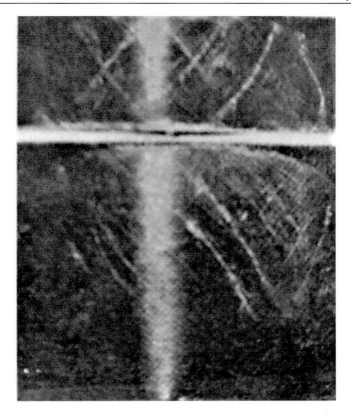

FIGURE 10.4   A horizontally sliced cylinder of wax after a vertically directed compression test showing slip-lines that intersect at close to 90°. [A. Nadai, Theory of flow and fracture of solids, **1**, 2nd edn., McGraw-Hill Book Co. Inc. Used by permission]

FIGURE 10.5   Part of the lunar farside topography. The practised observer will note the many gross lineaments that trend from top L to bottom R, as well as the many others that trend from bottom L to top R. The crater in the upper, LH corner is Keeler, diameter 160 km. [Lunar Orbiter, NASA]

University of Lancaster. Our priorities were to study the Lunar Orbiter photographs, which were provided gratis by NASA's World Data Center A, as well as to acquire more space that would allow us to use the increasing amount of space-data being generated by the U.S.A. and the U.S.S.R. The move allowed my Unit to expand and study comparative planetology: for example, by comparing grid patterns seen on other planetary objects with those of the Moon and Earth.

Mapping the Grid around the Whole of the Moon

11

With a grant from the Natural Environment Research Council, I was able to employ a special team of students who came to Lancaster over their summer vacation in 1972 to measure the lengths of all the major lineaments that they could find on photographs that now covered the whole surface of the Moon. In this way, I was able to speed up the laborious mapping process; but I also valued the chance to employ independent mappers of the lunar grid. Having just completed degree courses in geology and related subjects, they were ideal for the job.

Each student measured the total length of lineaments on that part of a Lunar Orbiter photographic print (measuring 50 cm × 40 cm) that was viewed through a small sheet of acetate, momentarily fixed in position, that carried a grid of parallel scratches (Fig. 11.1). They were instructed not to measure any lineament that crossed any of the scratch-lines. In this programme I wished to compare the trends of all the gross Moon-wide lineaments. However, those special, gross lineaments that are sub-radially oriented around Mare Imbrium were removed for separate analysis, to allow the general systems A, B and C (the latter system trending N-S) to be compared more easily around the globe. Starting from a base-line, the acetate was then rotated about its centre by successive increments of 10 deg. of azimuth. The measurement process was repeated for each azimuth until all possible directions had been covered once. The centre mark on the acetate was then shifted to a different location on the same photograph and the measuring process re-started. In every location, measurements covered an area, small enough to be regarded as flat, within a spherical cap that measured 15 degrees of arc selenocentric (Moon centred). In essence, this routine was a sampling device that, I considered, would represent the whole lunar surface sufficiently well for our purposes.

By the end of the summer, my Research Associate R. Fryer and I were able to examine the outcome of all this work. Fryer[23] developed a computerised method of rectifying all the mapping so that the total lengths of lineaments in each set direction and for each 15 degree region could be plotted in the form of a rose diagram. Each of the 50 rose diagrams was then plotted on the surface of a spherical globe (Fig. 11.2).

DOI: 10.1201/9781003181279-11

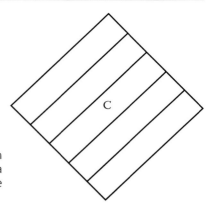

FIGURE 11.1   Parallel scratches on a square patch of five, equal area strips that were prepared on a sheet of clear acetate. The point C marks the centre of rotation used in our statistical tests. [G.Fielder]

FIGURE 11.2   Rose diagrams of regional lineament directions, plotted on a sphere, showing the trends of the grid system on the far side of the Moon. [G. Fielder, R. Fryer et al[35]]

For the first time, the trends of different families of the lunar grid system, across the near and far sides of the Moon, were revealed. These new, independent observations showed that systems A and B were prominent in the majority of lunar regions. In particular, around the whole of the equator, these strongly developed families of septa - the gross lineaments - intersected one another at an average (north-facing) dihedral angle of about 90°, with a large spread of ±10°. In practice, the angles of intersection of the

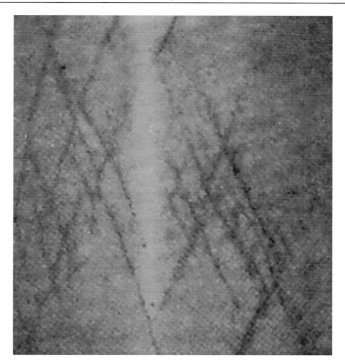

FIGURE 11.3 Slip lines in a cylinder of marble that has been subjected to vertical (axial) compression. Note that the upper (and lower) dihedral angles of intersection of the slip lines (or latent strike-slip faults) are much less than in the case of the wax cylinders shown in Fig. 10.4 because the internal friction of the wax is less than that of the marble. The Moon's pattern of joints or fractures is closer to that of the wax. This possibly indicates a small angle of internal friction in the lunar rocks at the time when they first yielded to meridional pressures. Perhaps the deeper rocks were plasticised, through heating, at the time of fracture. [Used by permission, as in caption of Fig. 10.4}

families A and B would vary as a result of inhomogeneities in the lunar crust and, possibly, because of temperature differences between different regions. In theory, a general principal crustal pressure, oriented N-S, could lead to two main sets of fracture directions that are symmetrically disposed around any meridian (Fig. 11.3). However, we noted that, in polar regions, the rose diagrams displayed a wide variety of lineament directions: in these areas, the stresses that caused the fracturing of the lunar materials appeared to have been relatively disorganised as to direction.

The theory predicts that tension fractures could develop in the meridional direction. It is in, or close to, this direction that some major lunar faults are to be found. Spurr[4] termed them selenofaults because of their similarity to geofaults (long faults

FIGURE 11.4   Long lunar faults, sometimes called selenofaults, are seen here in the Rheita Valley and again in the Metius to Piccolomini region. Rheita, butting into the Valley and sporting a central peak, is 70 km in diameter. Piccolomini (87 km), partly shown at the top L, also has a central peak. Metius, near to the centre of the picture, is the same size as Piccolomini. Notice that the floor of Young (71 km), south of Rheita, has been downfaulted by the Rheita Valley. [Adapted from E. Whitaker et al., Rectified Lunar Atlas, University of Arizona Press (1963), Plate 26b (L)]

that affect the relief of the Earth's surface). In some instances, selenofaults run for hundreds of kilometres (Fig. 11.4). The best way to identify the faults is to observe the same region under both sunrise and sunset conditions; but the angle of illumination can be critical. Alter[24] described some selenofaults; and I discussed selenofaults[21] in "Lunar Geology".

Faulting and the Rotation of the Moon

12

Selenofaults do not necessarily arise in simple, dip-slip motion. Some of them trend sub-radially with respect to Mare Nectaris and other maria and might better be described as rift valleys. In the case of Mare Imbrium, while some of the best developed, gross lineaments are associated with fracturing in the direction of system A, there are other,

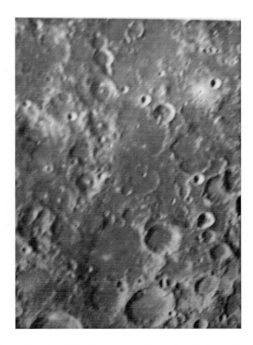

FIGURE 12.1 The selenofault that runs nearly vertically from top to bottom of this photograph and dissects it runs to the RHS of the peaked craters Vogel, Argelander, Airy and Donati. Here, the illumination is from the west (but see Fig. 12.2, taken under reversed illumination). [From the Photographic Lunar Atlas, Plate C6c (W), in Gerard P. Kuiper. © The University of Chicago, 1960, courtesy UC Press]

DOI: 10.1201/9781003181279-12

sub-radial lineaments that deviate progressively from the SE direction towards the S; and these appear to present as graben. The 450 km long fault running, roughly, from Vogel to Donati to Werner, shown in both morning and afternoon illumination in Figs. 12.1 and 12.2, is oriented along a meridian and could have been assisted, in its development, by reduced E–W pressures (or even tensions). The Altai scarp (Fig. 12.3) is a curving se-lenofault, only part of which trends in a northernly direction.

Shorter faults, such as the Straight Wall, the fault in Lacus Mortis (Figs. 12.4a and b), the fault in Boscovitch (Fig. 12.5) and the fault (Figs. 12.6a and b) close to the western

FIGURE 12.2   The same faulting system as shown in fig 12.1, but seen under illumination from the east. The downdropped trough has a generally darker floor than its surroundings. [From the Photographic Lunar Atlas, C6d (P), in Gerard P. Kuiper. © The University of Chicago 1960, courtesy UC Press]

FIGURE 12.3 The Altai scarp under a setting Sun. [Adapted from E. Whitaker, et al., Rectified Lunar Atlas, University of Arizona Press (1963), Plate 19d (W)]

(a)   (b)

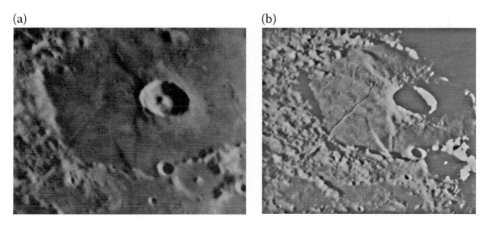

FIGURE 12.4 (a) A complex fault of dip-slip and rille in the southern part of Lacus Mortis as photographed under morning illumination. (The rille may be seen under higher lighting.) The crater Burg, 39 km in diameter, is close to the middle of Lacus Mortis. [From the Photographic Lunar Atlas, Plate C2e (P). Edited by Gerard P. Kuiper. © The University of Chicago 1960, courtesy UC Press]. (b) The same fault photographed under afternoon illumination. [From the Photographic Lunar Atlas, Plate C2a (W). Edited by Gerard P. Kuiper. © The University of Chicago 1960, courtesy UC Press]

FIGURE 12.5 Another complex fault, part dip-slip and part rille, in Boscovitch. Under morning light the dip-slip part casts a shadow. [From the Photographic Lunar Atlas, Plate C4a (P). Edited by Gerard P. Kuiper, © The University of Chicago 1960, courtesy UC Press]. The same fault shows as a bright band in the afternoon (Fig. 9.2). Boscovitch, near to the centre of the picture, is the dark-floored crater that contains the short fault.

(a)   (b)

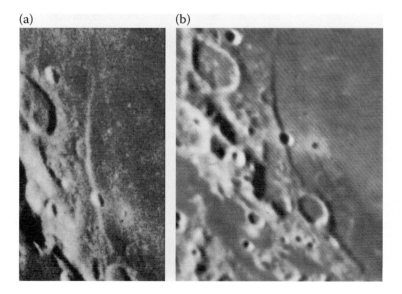

FIGURE 12.6 (a) The dip-slip fault (morning view) in the west of Mare Humorum passes through a crater, Liebig F, (diameter 9 km) but bypasses a similar sized, elongated crater at the edge of the upthrow. These craters may be compared under conditions of reversed illumination in this figure [From the Photographic Lunar Atlas, Plate E6b (P). Edited by Gerard P. Kuiper. C The University of Chicago 1960, courtesy UC Press] and in Fig. 12.6(b). (b) This shows the same area in an afternoon photograph. [From the Photographic Lunar Atlas, Plate E6a (M). Edited by Gerard P. Kuiper. © The University of Chicago 1960, courtesy UC Press]

(a)   (b)

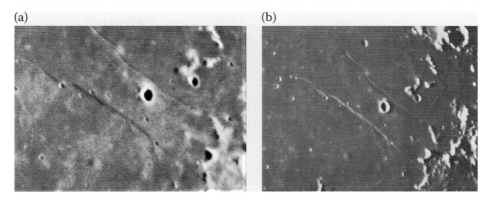

FIGURE 12.7   (a) The complex Cauchy fault in morning light that puts the fault face in shadow. [Adapted from E. Whitaker et al., Rectified Lunar Atlas, University of Arizona Press (1963), Plate 14b(L)]. (b) The Cauchy fault seen with a lighter face in afternoon light; but also, in parts, as a rille, particularly near to the westen end. [From the Photographic Lunar Atlas, Plate B4b (W). Edited by Gerard P. Kiuper. © The University of Chicago 1960, courtesy UC Press]

margin of Mare Humorum, all trend in directions not far from the directions of meridians; but the Cauchy fault (Figs. 12.7a and b) which, like the one in Lacus Mortis, is a complex of dip-slip and rille, trends in the direction of system A. So, in specific cases, regional stresses have evidently contributed to the overall stress regime and there cannot be a universal rule that lunar dip-slip faults follow meridians. The complex faults show that rilles can originate in both tensile and strike-slip regimes, the latter becoming tensile in the manner that I have argued[49] for the Ariadaeus rille. (A fuller discussion of the lunar tensile regime will follow in section 36.)

The theory I have put forward requires every meridian around the Moon to be subject to roughly equal N-S pressure. That would not be possible for a synchronous Moon stressed only by the attraction of the Earth. Another factor that relates to the stressing of a planetary body is its rate of spin. Planetary materials are not generally rigid over long periods: they have a range of elasticity. While the tendency to sphericity of a planet is caused by gravity, spin can cause a sphere to deform and become an oblate spheroid (Fig. 12.8). In the spin-up process of a real, non-rigid planet the length of the equator will tend to increase and the polar axis will tend to shorten, so that a cross-section through the poles will tend to change from a circle to an ellipse. The ellipticity will increase as the rate of spin increases and decrease as the spin rate decreases. It is clear that the crustal stresses caused by a spinning Moon will show a symmetry with respect to the polar axis.

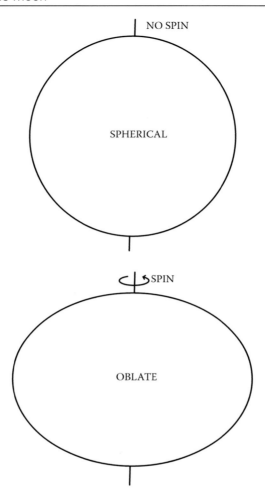

FIGURE 12.8   The deformation of a non-rigid planet as a result of moderate rotation about its axis. Here, material is prevented from tearing off, along a tangent to the surface, by its cohesive and body strengths and the centripetal force that is provided by gravity. [G. Fielder]

Did the Moon spin more quickly in the past? Even a synchronous Moon that, in the recent past, was closer to the Earth would have turned more quickly on its axis. And the stresses generated by spinning alone would have been greater, then, than those of the present epoch, as would the propensity for fractures to develop in the Moon's crust.

The Origin of the Lunar Grid System 13

In order to look further at the problem of the origin of the Moon-wide fracture pattern that led, I believe, to the grid of lineaments that we see today, I invited P. Gash, from the Geology Department of Imperial College London, to join the Lunar and Planetary Unit. Already qualified in rock mechanics, he agreed to take as his PhD topic an investigation as to whether the two mechanisms of Earth-raised lunar tides and rotation rate of the Moon were instrumental in producing the lunar grid system. Specifically, Gash developed a theory that enabled him to describe the stress patterns that would be produced in the crust of the Moon as a result of

    a. Earth tidal forces acting on a synchronously rotating Moon;
    b. the Moon in free rotation; and
    c. a combination of the tidal mechanism and free rotation.

He applied the theory to models of a lunar crust having a thickness that was small in comparison with its mean radius of curvature. First, Gash examined crusts that were unconstrained in their displacements. Then, he examined crusts that were restricted by the underlying mantle. Finally, for these models, he calculated the crustal stresses and the consequential patterns of potential fracturing across the lunar surface.

At the present time, the Earth generates a maximum tensile stress in the central area of the Moon's near side of about 1.5 bar at perigee and about 1 bar at apogee. These stresses fall short – probably by a factor of 1000 – of those required to fracture consolidated lunar rocks. Gash[25] noted that, if the lunar fractures were initiated by tides raised by the Earth, rather than by any other mechanism (such as convection in the Moon) "the Moon would have to have been in an orbit closer to the Earth than its present one". But the stress fields produced in case (a) were, clearly, not able to generate the N–S oriented crustal pressures required to initiate a fracture pattern similar to that seen in the lunar grid system.

For case (b), Gash allotted a tensile strength to the lunar crust and considered a model with two different degrees of restriction of the crust. He obtained equations for the time-independent principal stresses in the rotating crust. In both model crusts, the stresses close to the surface proved to be tensile. However, as depth increases so does the overburden of rock; and, for increasing depth, he predicted shear fracturing in the mid-latitudes of the Moon. This shearing would be developed most strongly, he found, around the equator. Also in mid-latitudes, tensile fractures would trend in the N–S direction. In

DOI: 10.1201/9781003181279-13

polar regions, tension fracturing would prevail, shear fractures would be absent, and the trends of lineaments would focus at the poles.

In the words of Gash[25], "depending on the depth, this model predicts NE–SW, NW–SE and N–S joints over the greater part of the Moon's crust, with a gradational change to only N–S joints nearer to the poles and non-systematic joints at the poles". This model predicts a fracture pattern that is, with some reserve for the high, mid-latitudes, remarkably close to the lineament pattern that we mapped over large areas of the Moon.

In order to test case(c), which combines tidal and rotational mechanisms, Gash superimposed the tidal stresses in a synchronous Moon on the stresses that, he reasoned, might well have resided in the Moon in terms of strains built up following an earlier orbit in free rotation. With reasonable assumptions about the residual stresses and the physical properties of the Moon's crust, he constructed the trajectories of the resultant principal stresses. In the equatorial and mid-latitude regions, the predicted fracture pattern is close to that of a free-rotation model; but, at latitudes higher than 40° or 50°, the calculated stress pattern diverges from that at lower latitudes. Critically, Gash pointed out that this model would be applicable if the lineament families of the observed grid did not converge at the poles.

In summary, case (a) must be rejected as the main cause of the grid system. The best diagnostic to distinguish case (b) from case (c) lies in what is seen in the higher mid-latitudes and, in particular, in polar areas of the Moon: do the trends of lineaments focus at, or near to, the poles or do they not?

Although the lineament trends mapped by my students in the regions around, and greater than, latitudes ±60° do not show signs of focusing at the lunar poles, the sampling method used in my analysis was probably too coarse to reach a satisfactory conclusion about such focusing. A better approach might be to scrutinise photographs of the polar regions and record the directions of the lineaments seen in those areas. Using the polar photographs reproduced on pages 1 and 144 of the Clementine Atlas of the Moon (1994), I sketched the most obvious lineaments (ridges, troughs and, frequently, chains of craters) in both the northern and southern polar areas (Figs. 13.1a and b). The lineaments show no tendency to trend towards the respective poles.

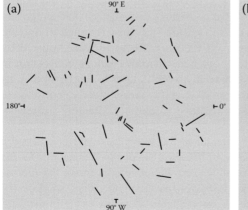 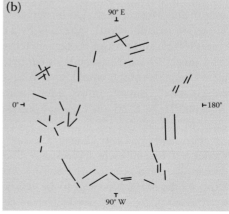

FIGURE 13.1   (a) Polar lineaments in the vicinity of the Moon's north polar cap. [G. Fielder]. (b) Polar lineaments around the Moon's south polar cap. [G. Fielder]

So while the free rotation mechanism appears to have a very significant influence in forming the fracture pattern around most of the Moon's surface, the observed lack of convergance of lineament systems at the poles implies that the free rotation model is not the sole cause of the underlying fracture system. To quote Gash[25] "the present tidal stresses could serve marginally to augment the residual stresses to values above the strength of the crust and, thus, act as a trigger for primary fracturing".

Of course, it would be as well to bear in mind that departures from the fracture patterns predicted by this theory are likely to occur, not least because of compositional variations in the lunar crustal rocks and the possible presence, locally, of special stress systems arising from the larger impacts or even from convective processes. With this proviso, it may be concluded that the gross lineaments arose in deep fractures initiated by both the free rotational and the tidal mechanisms.

Melting in the Moon

14

Potentially, the lunar grid system presents evidence on the history of the Earth-Moon system that is independent of the classical arguments that have been invoked to explain the lunar secular acceleration and to predict the past proximity of the Moon to the Earth. As the Earth is 81.3 times more massive than the Moon, the Earth's tide-raising force at the Moon is significantly more than the Moon's tide-raising force at the Earth. Part of the energy involved in the tidal interaction will be converted, through friction, to heat. Since, in the past, the distance between the Earth and Moon has probably been less than at present and, since a tide-raising force between any two gravitating bodies is proportional to the inverse cube of the distance between them, one might envisage a situation in which the lunar rocks actually melted as a result of early, intensive tidal interaction.

As early as 1968, Surveyor VII analysed a rock fragment that was, roughly, 27 km beyond the northern rim of Tycho. The rock (Fig. 14.1) was found to be anorthositic in composition and similar in reflectivity to the lunar highlands. Anorthosites represent chemically differentiated rocks; and they imply heating in the Moon. The Apollo 15 (1971) and 17 (1972) missions were used to measure the heat flow from the interior of the Moon and found it to be about 3×10^{-6} W.cm^{-2} and 2×10^{-6} W.cm^{-2} – roughly half that from the Earth's interior. That was higher than expected from the Moon. Another relatively light coloured rock sample returned from the Apollo 11 site in Mare Tranquillitatis was thought to be an exotic (a fragment that had been transferred far from its natural setting) anorthosite. In 1972, the Apollo 16 mission enabled astronauts to return rock samples directly from a highland site. One of the Apollo 16 anorthosites was found, later, to have an age of 4.4×10^9 years. Like the other anorthosites, this specimen must have crystallised from a liquid magma. The date of crystallisation establishes that at least part of the Moon was hot enough to be molten very early in the Moon's history.

Most of the rock samples that the Apollo 16 astronauts returned from the Cayley/Descartes region of the highlands were composed, largely, of the rock-forming mineral plagioclase which forms white, lath-shaped crystals, common in basic igneous rocks. Analyses of the lunar plagioclases show that they are enriched in the rare earth element europium. Following extensive early melting, plagioclase must have floated up from the mantle and cooled to form the Moon's crust, enriched in europium.[26] Other laboratory dating and analysis, this time of returned mare lavas, showed that they erupted later, between 3×10^9 and 4×10^9 years ago, probably as a result of partial

DOI: 10.1201/9781003181279-14

FIGURE 14.1   Cracks in a block of rock close to, and photographed by, Surveyor VII. The block is a little over one foot in length. Note that part of each crack is paralleled by the strong lineations in the uncracked face. (Ignore the uniformly vertical scan lines.) [NASA/JPL]

melting of pockets of rock in the mantle. These basalts are depleted in europium, indicating that the plagioclase had acquired the europium from the parent magmas.

It becomes clear that, to produce all the crustal material of the lunar highlands, which might attain a thickness of some tens of kilometres (estimated from the Apollo seismometry) on the near side of the Moon, it is necessary to find a means of melting extensive volumes of the underlying rocks. Furthermore, the dating of the crust meant that this melting had to be achieved soon after the time of formation of the Moon itself, generally estimated to have been somewhat more than 4.5×10^9 years ago. Various attempts to clarify the nature of the heating mechanism have been made. The half-life of a radioactive substance is the period over which half of its bulk will decay into its daughter elements. The concentrations of K_{40} (half-life 1.25×10^9 years), U_{238} (4.5×10^9 years) and Th_{232} (1.4×10^{10} years) would have produced most heat later than the required early heating period. However, had it been close to the Earth, tidal heating in the Moon would have been a strong candidate for heating it in its early days.

The Origin of the Moon

15

Also of relevance to the early heating problem is the way the Moon was made. I think that the most promising of the several theories on the origin of the Moon that have been proffered since the publication of G. Darwin's Classical Theory[72] is one involving a titanic collision between the early Earth and a hypothetical proto-planet called Theia. (See, for example, Hartmann et al.[27]) Possibly up to 7000 km across, Thea, which might have been of water-ice and denser materials, collided with the Earth at a glancing angle, increasing the Earth's rate of spin and vaporising much of both Theia and an outer portion of the Earth. The evidence is that this might have happened some 4.4×10^9 years ago. Much volatile matter would have been lost.

The nineteenth century astronomer E. Roche showed that a fluid satellite orbiting a large planet could approach the planet no closer than a certain distance (the Roche limit) before tidal forces (see section 6) would pull the satellite apart. The alternative process, envisaged as an enormous cloud of cooling, condensing matter and solids from the Theia catastrophe is quite different. The respective densities and cohesive properties of the Earth and of all the other objects involved would have to be taken into account; and the mean density of a growing proto-Moon could differ at different times. Nevertheless, I reason that the differing gravitational attractions of the Earth across each condensing object and between all the different objects would limit any significant accumulation of the objects, due to their mutual gravitational attractions, to orbits that are quite distant from the Earth. On their outward journey, smaller objects would have to pass their Roche limit before any significant mutual accumulation could occur.

The largest of these integrations would form the proto-Moon. The speed of accumulation would be an important factor in determining how hot a proto-body would be. With its augmenting size, the proto-Moon would attract more incoming mass. The intense tidal stressing of both the proto-Moon and the Earth would add, through internal friction, to the temperatures of each object, at the same time driving them further apart. The early Moon's crust of plagioclase would form through underlying convective motions, differentiation and further cooling. At distances of, perhaps, some tens of thousands of kilometres from the Earth, when the newly formed crust of the Moon was sufficiently cool, it would sustain fractures produced by the large stresses it was experiencing. These fractures would be the precursors of the lunar grid system.

Density differences within the Moon would enable gravitational couples to slow its axial rotation until it became a synchronous satellite. Today, billions of years after its birth, and at the mean distance of 384400 km from the Earth, the Moon still carries imprints of its tumultuous history.

DOI: 10.1201/9781003181279-15

Fine Lineaments and Their Significance

16

In 1964, G. Kuiper, then Director of the Lunar and Planetary Laboratory of the University of Arizona, invited me to assist in the interpretation of some of the 4000-odd images that the probe Ranger 7 acquired, and transmitted to Earth in real time, before crashing in Mare Cognitum (Fig. 16.1) on 30 July of that year. The first strange details that I noticed were the striations of the lunar terrain that was imaged just before impact.

With the collaboration of P. Rogers of Imperial College, J. Guest, L. Wilson and I, working at the University of London Observatory, had melted basic terrestrial lavas in a furnace and then outgassed them in a vacuum chamber.[28] This caused the lavas, releasing their volatile components, to bubble up and form very porous, underdense structures (Fig. 16.2). These were the sort of lavas that I had expected to be present on the surface of the atmosphereless Moon. Using a specially constructed, long-arm goniphotometer (Fig. 16.3), we found that these simulated lunar lavas did not scatter light in the way observed in any part of the Moon's surface. Light scattering functions closer to those of the real lunar rocks were obtained by smashing up the simulated rocks to form a range of particle sizes; just as long-term meteoric impacts might have done. Wilson, who had consulted B. Hapke in the U.S.A., constructed a small proton accelerator as part of his PhD Thesis. He used his accelerator to further damage the particles by proton bombardment, since solar radiation would have damaged rocks exposed on the lunar surface in like fashion. Testing these materials photometrically produced light scattering functions similar to those of the Moon. Following these experiments, I had expected the regolith (lunar soil) to be granular, with a range of particle sizes, and largely structureless.

On the contrary, at a scale of less than 1 m, the regolith that I saw in the Ranger images looked as if a rake had been drawn through it creating fine, straight ridge-and-trough lineaments, rather like a ploughed field. Also of interest to me were the elongated craters that I found with their longest axes running in the same direction as the local lineaments. At first, I wondered if the image-recording process might have blurred the pictures. Then I noticed other craters in the same field that were circular and crisply defined; and I realised that the fine lineamentation of the terrain was real.

DOI: 10.1201/9781003181279-16

FIGURE 16.1   Western Mare Cognitum. [From the Photographic Lunar Atlas, Plate E5a (M), in Gerard P. Kuiper. (Eds.), © The Universiy of Chicago, 1960, courtesy UC Press.] Ranger VII crashed in the unlit part of Mare Cognitum to the R of the 7 km diameter crater Bonpland E that is half-way up the picture and is casting a long shadow into the morning terminator. G. Kuiper, E. Shoemaker and H. Urey formed the scientific team charged with analysing the Ranger VII data. After G.P. Kuiper's death in 1973, the International Astronomical Union's Nomenclature Committee re-named this crater Kuiper, in recognition of his considerable contributions to lunar studies.

A year later, when I was studying the last frames taken from Ranger 9 before impact on the floor of the giant crater Alphonsus (108 km diameter), I found similar fine lineaments (Fig. 16.4) composed of ridges, depressions and crater alignments. They crossed the hummocky walls and shallow, depressed floors of what looked like degraded craters imprinted in the floor of Alphonsus. Here, there were clearly two sets of intersecting, fine lineaments. I reported this observation in 1966 at a NATO Conference organised by S.K. Runcorn at the University of Newcastle-upon-Tyne and I reproduced this picture, with some notes.[29] These fine lineaments crossed one another at angles that were not very different from a right angle and seemed to cut through all features except for small, sharply defined, circular craters.

Over the years 1966 to 1968, the Surveyor soft-landers and, in particular, the Lunar Orbiter spacecraft, revealed an abundance of fine lineaments at different localities across the Moon. Even the walls (Fig. 16.5) of Tycho, the well-known, relatively recent 100 km diameter ray-crater in the Moon's southern hemisphere and, again, the wall (Fig. 16.6) of Prinz (diameter 46 km), are criss-crossed with fine lineaments. Surprisingly, so are the Alps (Fig. 16.7); and a photograph of Mt. Hadley (Fig. 16.8) taken from the ground by astronaut James Irwin reveals criss-crossing

FIGURE 16.2   Crucible of outgassed basalt. [G. Fielder, J. Guest, L. Wilson and P. Rogers[28]]

lineaments, one set more conspicuous than the other, on the distant mountains. In 1969, N. Armstrong and E. Aldrin stepped down from the landing module of Apollo 11 onto the regolith of Mare Tranquillitatis and photographed the local landscape (Fig. 16.9) showing that, even here, there were fine lineaments criss-crossing the mare regolith. Changing to a terra (highland) type of landscape (Fig 16.10), where Apollo 16 astronaut J. Young photographed the surface, fine lineaments were again seen to criss-cross the regolith. Even when J. Irwin stood in Mare Imbrium above a tiny crater measuring perhaps 20 cm across (Fig. 16.12: see below) fine, intersecting lineaments were in evidence. Here, each set of lineaments had a wavelength of 1cm or so. In fact,

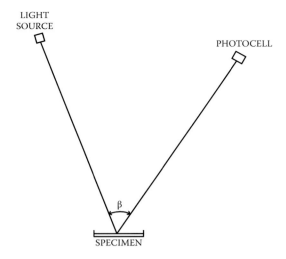

FIGURE 16.3 Our goniphotometer is a device in which the light source and the receiver, a photocell, are each supported by rigid arms that rotate in a fixed plane about an axis passing through the specimen. The arms are long enough to enable the angle beta to approach zero, in spite of the finite size of the light source and receiver. Such a circumstance enables one to model full Moon conditions. [G. Fielder]

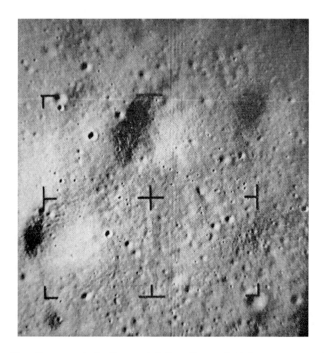

FIGURE 16.4 Fine lineaments in the undulating floor of Alphonsus, recorded by Ranger IX (Ignore vertical stripes). [NASA]

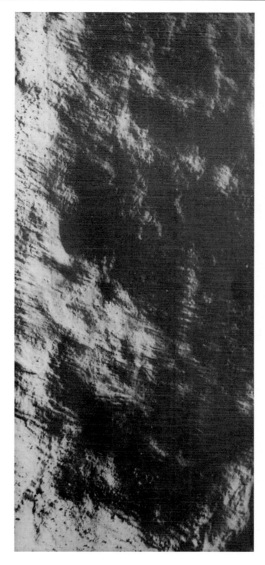

FIGURE 16.5 Fine lineaments < 50m wide, on the NE outer rim of Tycho. Note that they are intersected by other lineaments. [Lunar Orbiter V, NASA]

FIGURE 16.6   Criss-crossing fine lineaments in the wall of Prinz, 46 km diameter. [Lunar Orbiter V, NASA]

many of the new, high-resolution scenes that were recorded under favourable solar illumination revealed a surface that was not disordered, churned up by the impacts of innumerable meteoroids over the ages, as I had expected. Instead, it seemed to me that the Moon had been furrowed, and cross-furrowed, in an ordered way; and that it was necessary to explain why these imprints had persisted to the present day. Finally, I am puzzled by the photograph, taken from Surveyor VII, that records fractured rocks (Fig. 16.11) that are not far from Tycho: an analysis of these fracture directions is unsupportive of the theory that the rock blocks were tossed there. Could these rocks have been formed more or less in situ? In summary, not only the gross lineaments but also the fine lineaments of the Moon seem to me to define a remarkable and general property of the lunar surface.

What can be the cause of these ubiquitous, fine-scale lineaments? At the 1966 NATO Conference, I suggested that the lunar terrain that displayed these highly ordered systems must be activated by moonquakes drawing their energy from the tides raised by the Earth. It seemed that the Moon was still showing signs of widespread

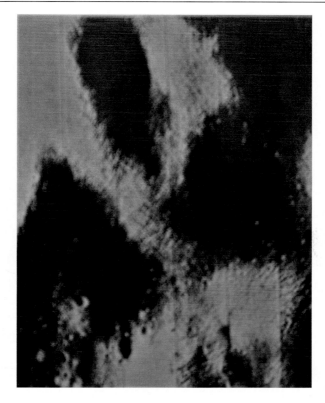

FIGURE 16.7   Mutually intersecting, fine lineaments in the lunar Alps. [Lunar Orbiter V, NASA]

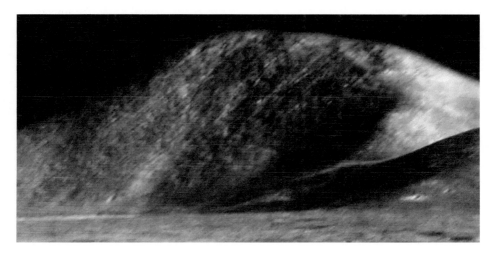

FIGURE 16.8   Lineaments of Mount Hadley photographed during the Apollo 15 mission in 1971 by astronaut J. Irwin. Careful study will show that a weaker set of lineaments intersects the more strongly developed ones. [NASA]

FIGURE 16.9   Fine intersecting lineaments in the surface of Mare Tranquillitatis, near to the landing site of Apollo 11. [NASA]

FIGURE 16.10   More criss-crossing fine lineaments, this time in the Descartes highlands. Picture taken by the Apollo 16 astronaut J. Young in 1972. [NASA]

FIGURE 16.11 Surveyor VII photograph of intersecting fractures running through a field of rock blocks. [NASA/JPL]

FIGURE 16.12 Here, each family of intersecting lineaments displays a wavelength of the order of 1cm. Most of these fine lineaments are, clearly, not caused by ejecta from the small crater shown in Mare Imbrium. [J. Irwin, Apollo 15, NASA]

activity, contrary to the views postured by many scientists at the time. As Gash and I have proposed, these tidal forces, although far too weak to fracture previously un-fractured rocks, are probably sufficiently energetic even now, particularly at perigee, to re-activate older grid fractures underlying the regolith.

The Ages of the Lunar Surface Features

17

Age determinations of returned mare lavas range from about 3×10^9 years to about 4×10^9 years, whereas lunar impact melts that were found in highland regions (and elsewhere) yield a range of only 3.8×10^9 years to 4×10^9 years (Fig. 17.1). This result seems to require the flux of impacting meteoroids to be constrained in a narrow time corridor and to cease more recently than 3.8×10^9 years ago. Clearly, this conclusion is not inconsistent with the sparsity of craters in the maria. If the early bombardment really did terminate at about that time, surface features developed later would have been left largely unscathed by major impacts.

To investigate the origin of the objects that produced the majority of the lunar impact craters, Strom et al.[86] examined the frequencies of occurrence of asteroids of a given size, but belonging to different groups, and related these distributions to the size-frequency distributions of lunar craters in the highlands and, separately, in the maria. These authors found that the "main belt asteroids" (population 1) showed a distribution similar to that of the bulk of lunar craters that were formed earlier than 3.9×10^9 years ago; whereas the much lower (but steady) flux of "near Earth asteroids" (population 2) generated most of the lunar impact craters that were formed since $(3.8 \text{ to } 3.7) \times 10^9$ years ago, such as those that represent post-mare impacts.

Indeed, the major impact that, it is generally mooted, created Tycho seems to date to several 10^8 years ago since it must pre-date the local lavas that Strom and Fielder[30] described: these lavas flowed down the inner and outer walls of Tycho and welled up to cover its original floor. An essentially similar age, and set of events, appear to apply to Aristarchus (40 km diameter) and, possibly, to other ray-craters. Pictures, and the relevant details, will be given in Section 28. Realistically, in order to accommodate the presence of large, well-defined craters like Tycho, one must assume that, occasionally, large meteoroids struck the Moon up to 3.4×10^9 years later than the time when the intense early bombardment terminated; and that, additionally, a rain of minor meteoroids continued to the present day, evidenced partly in the detections by the lunar seismometers of those quakes that tend to occur at random intervals of time.

Whereas features of the Earth's surface are subject to extrinsic erosion and denudation through the persistent action of water and wind, it appears that, since the early

DOI: 10.1201/9781003181279-17

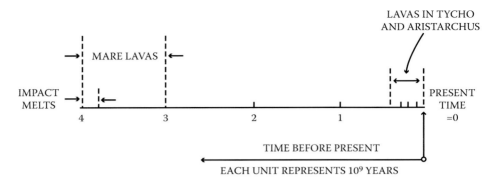

FIGURE 17.1 Time-line showing the deduced ages of lunar lavas. [G. Fielder]

bombardment, the lunar surface has been subjected to a much slower extrinsic erosion process caused by the accretion of fast moving micrometeoroids. Each one that collides with the Moon may dislodge 100 to 1000 times its own volume of lunar rock. (By comparison, thermal fracturing and erosion by cosmic ray particles are relatively unimportant processes.)

From observed rates of accretion of micrometeoroids in the vicinity of the Earth, I deduced[31] the limits of the mean accretion rate at the Moon's surface and set an upper limit of 10^{-6} cm per year for the volume of lunar surface material that would be eroded per unit surface area per annum. Transportation of eroded debris by gravitational and electrostatic processes alone is an extremely slow process. Even seismicity, which assists gravity to transport eroded products downslope, would need to act for 10^8 years to erase features of relief 1 m. The rays (Fig. 1.1) of certain craters, composed of small, secondary craters and associated particulate deposits[32] have remained visible for several 10^8 years. Of course, the rates of extrinsic erosion and denudation might well have differed, in the past, from those at the present time. Intrinsic erosion caused by tidal action must have been important, in the past, since the consequences of tidal action include faulting, heating and igneous activity. Such actions will have been weaker in recent time. Fine ridge lineaments of, for example, 10m height would be expected to remain visible for at least 10^9 years, whether or not aided by the continuing action of minor moonquakes.

It is commonly reasoned that the lunar regolith was generated, over the millenia, by a process called "impact gardening". Extrusion of volcanic materials that outgassed upon reaching a point close to the surface could be another important process that was active in generating regolith. Although the outgassing might be indicative of the possible presence of water (see section 45), at least at depth, the surface of the regolith is essentially dry, but it is not like dry sand or dust. Since the time of the earliest softlanders, close up studies of the mechanical properties of the regolith proved that, although granular and fragmental, it displayed a cohesive strength that allowed the walls of a trench (Fig. 17.2) dug using automatic equipment carried by Surveyor 7, to sustain angles of repose close to 90°. In our simulations of broken, outgassed lunar lavas, the

FIGURE 17.2   Trench dug by the scoop device of Surveyor VII. [NASA]

cohesion of the regolith was to be explained by the effective interlocking of irregularly-shaped particles. Dry though it was, the regolith did not flow to establish a smaller angle of repose in the way that might apply to a pile of dry sand. So, in this model, once shuffled into small ridges by movements along fractures beneath it, the regolith would probably stay put for a long time.

The Origins of Small Craters

18

Dykes are created when liquid magmas ascend through a planetary crust by prising open and filling fractures before solidifying (Fig. 18.1). The magmas rise under hydrostatic pressure. In the special case of the Moon, where there is essentially no atmospheric pressure and uncommonly small overburdens provided by the regolith, the final stage of the ascent of a liquid dyke would be interrupted by the explosive release of any contained gases into the vacuum.[28] In the process, small craters would be formed by the sudden dispersal of near-surface materials accompanied by the collapse of some of the regolith. Many of the chains of small craters on the Moon were, in my view, formed in this manner. The chains (Fig. 18.2) are, most commonly, parallel to the local ridge and trough lineaments and, indeed, contribute to the lineament pattern. These chains are most unlikely to have been produced by other mechanisms, such as secondary impact cratering. The intrusion of magmas along strike-slip faults might indicate that the pressure across the faults had reduced since their early formation. In the following account, I shall refer to any crater formed as the result of an internal process as an endocrater.

Most students of the Moon now accept, from the largely circumstantial evidence, that the majority of its craters, of all sizes, originated by meteoric impact. I shall show, first, that that view is not necessarily correct for the smaller craters. Since the 1960s, after spacecraft acquired close-up photographs of the lunar surface, most professional astronomers deduced that a small proportion of all the craters was of internal origin; while many assiduous amateur observers had recognized volcanic edifices on the Moon well before that time.

It was of concern to me in the 1960s that scientists were regularly using counts of the total number of small craters in a lunar region as a means of estimating both its relative, and absolute, age; for, although many scientists did allow for craters that they recognised as secondary impact craters, they tended to make the assumption that most of the remaining craters counted were primary impact craters. Clearly, if crater counts were to be used for dating, there was a need to specify the proportions of exogenic (impact) and endogenic (internally formed) craters in any part of the lunar surface.

When Kuiper asked me, in 1967, to return to his Lunar and Planetary Laboratory (LPL) to engage in some further research, I saw an opportunity to use the latest space data that were already available there to re-examine the prevailing views on the origins of the lunar craters; and I flew to Tucson, with my family, late in 1967, to spend a year in the western United States.

DOI: 10.1201/9781003181279-18

FIGURE 18.1   This wedge-shaped lava forms the top of a dyke that has been squeezed up a fracture through a lava flow in Sunset Crater National Monument, Arizona. [G. Fielder]

Some years before that, E. Whitaker and family had followed a similar course but, in his case, that led to his staying permanently at the LPL. Before he left Britain, he was Director of the Lunar Section of the British Astronomical Association, a position which he had to relinquish and wanted me to fill. I did so for a short time until I also left for Arizona. During my honorary Directorship of the BAA's Lunar Section, I was able to meet, and discuss lunar matters with, amateur observers who called at the University of London Observatory. Those discussions brought me definite rewards.

In Arizona, the Whitakers liked to picnic in the desert where designated areas each had their stand-pipe for fresh water, set among the saguaro and other cacti (Fig. 18.3). Together with other astronomers from the LPL, my family and I were able to enjoy these memorable occasions. Other free weekends were used to travel around and learn about the regional geology. One highlight for me was an expedition by car to the

FIGURE 18.2 Chains of small craters may be picked out near to the crater Delisle (diameter 25 km). The chains run predominantly in the two directions that cross, roughly, at right angles and that correspond to the directions A and B of the grid system. [Apollo 15, NASA]

Pinacate region of Mexico to find and examine a crater called Elegante (Fig 18.4a) which, with other craters, I had photographed from the air on a previous occasion. Elegante looked as if it could have been transported from the Moon! The crater was hard to find from the ground, because of its low rim (Fig 18.4b), as well as because of the total lack of surfaced roads through the desert scrub. The craters here were thought to be formed by multiple volcanic explosions involving ground water, possibly from the nearby Gulf of California. A second interesting crater, which I photographed (Fig. 18.5) on the earlier overflight, was actually named "Moon Crater", probably because of its central cone that was capped with its own crater.

Another highlight was a visit to the well-known Meteor Crater (Fig. 18.4c and d), northern Arizona, arranged by E. Shoemaker and V. Wilmarth of the U.S. Geological Survey at Flagstaff. I think it is very important to examine each of the two small craters Elegante and Meteor Crater and note that they were formed by totally different mechanisms. Meteor Crater is a well-documented impact crater. Elegante is an endocrater.

FIGURE 18.3   E. Whitaker and the author, who is pointing at an old saguaro in Lower Sabina Canyon, Arizona Desert. [B. Middlehurst]

The difficulty of using their appearances to distinguish between their origins will be obvious. J. MacCaulay, also from the USGS, flew me over the basaltic flows and crater fields of New Mexico and northern Arizona. Similar basaltic lava flows are common elsewhere: two flow types in Hawaii are illustrated in Fig. 18.6.

W. Elston from the University of New Mexico arranged another productive visit, this time to Battleship Rock (Fig. 18.7a), which is part of an extensive ignimbrite (ash) flow from the Valles Caldera (Fig. 18.7b). Although acidic in composition, this solidified flow with its included fiammées (small, aerodynamically shaped particles that are indicative of flow direction, Fig. 18.7c) led me to think how, in a basaltic environment, some of the lunar sinuous rilles might have been formed.

Shortly before I left for Arizona, I had published a paper "Tests for randomness in the distribution of lunar craters", using standard statistical methods.[33] In examining different populations of craters and, notably, the population within Ptolemaeus

(a)

(b)

(c)

(d)

FIGURE 18.4 (a) Elegante and cinder cones, Pinacates region, Mexico. [G. Fielder]. (b) The profile of the Elegante crater, shown on the skyline immediately to the left of the nearest saguaro, is not easy to find from the ground. [G. Fielder]. (c) Meteor (Barringer) Crater, Arizona, is about 1.2 km in diameter and the present depth is about 180 m. [G. Fielder]. (d) Profile of Meteor Crater. The ringwall rises to some 60m above the fairly level sur-roundings. [G. Fielder]

(diameter 164 km, Fig. 18.8), I concluded that (a) the craters examined are distributed non-randomly; and (b) at least some of the craters are very probably of internal origin. Becoming aware of my interest in lunar crater statistics, A. Marcus, working at the Statistical Laboratory, Cambridge University, contacted me at the University of London Observatory and suggested that we engage in a collaborative effort: he wanted a subject to which he could apply his statistics, while I wanted a statistician to suggest the best way to attack the problem of the segregation of impact craters from en-docraters. We met several times, at ULO and at Cambridge, hardened on a plan and published our joint paper[34] in 1967. The method, involving a statistical test, came in good time for me to adapt it to my work in the University of Arizona, where a further crucial statistical test was developed.

Remarkably, by using Marcus' improved method, it became possible to detect the chaining of craters even though the chains were not obvious to the eye. (Possibly, the craters in such chains were spaced too widely to allow their ready identification as geologically associated members.)

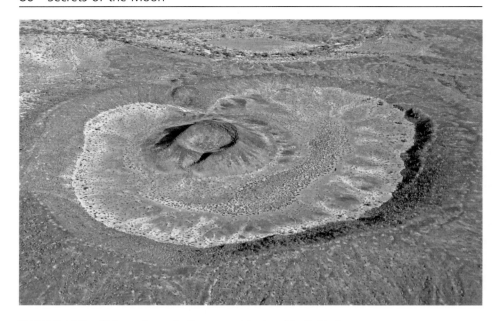

FIGURE 18.5   "Moon Crater", Pinacates, Mexico. [G. Fielder]

The mixing of different populations of craters (for example, the denser crater population of the lunar highlands and the less dense one in the maria) could introduce non-randomness to the results even if each separate population were random. Marcus noted that, in the lunar highlands, which are, technically, "saturated" with craters (Fig. 18.9), the overlapping of the large craters can introduce non-randomness – which may, or may not, represent the original distribution – into a population. Even different maria display differing number-densities (numbers per unit area) of craters. The most densely populated areas are in Mare Orientale, Sinus Medii, Mare Frigoris and Mare Foecunditatis, with between 20 and 30 craters larger than 700 m in diameter per 1000 km^2. By contrast, in Mare Tranquillitatis and Mare Smythii, crater numbers larger than 700 m diameter per 1000 km^2 are in single figures. For these reasons, and to maximise the specific information that would derive from each area studied, I decided to analyse the crater distribution in selected parts of each mare separately.

The analysis that I had in mind at the Lunar and Planetary Laboratory would be challenging in terms of manpower and G. Kuiper agreed to fund one of my London colleagues, R. Fryer, to join me in this project. I was also fortunate to be able to enlist further help from C. Titulaer, A. Herring and B. Wise. Using high-quality Lunar Orbiter photographs, the majority taken nearly vertically, we first engaged in test counts which served to check that there would be no significant observational losses of craters in the counting process. Together, we made one third of a million counts on 73,127 craters in 22 mare-type areas selected so as to avoid any area that crossed an obvious boundary between different crater populations.[35] Fryer generated special

FIGURE 18.6   G. Kuiper standing on a flow of pahoehoe lava that overlies a flow of aa lava in Hawaii. Being a little older and rougher than the pahoehoe lava, the aa lava has acquired a lighter coating as a result of lichen invasion. The Hawaiian word pahoehoe translates as "easy to walk over" whereas aa means "difficult to walk over". [G.Fielder]

computer programmes needed to process our manual counts of all the craters, most of which ranged in diameter between 100 m and 2000 m.

Maps were prepared on clear acetate placed in contact with the Lunar Orbiter prints: the centre of each crater was marked on the acetate with a black dot (Fig. 18.10). (Another kind of map, in which the craters were represented as black discs, was used in photometric studies of clustering of craters.) To facilitate the counts, the dot maps were copied photographically and enlarged to 45 cm × 58 cm. (Shrinkage of the photographic paper introduced errors that were found to be negligible.)

Interestingly, the crater number-density, adopted as the total number of craters >700 m in diameter per 1000 km^2 of lunar surface, varied by a factor of 6.6 between the smallest, and the largest, crater number-density of the 22 areas studied. A simple

(a)

(c)

(b)

FIGURE 18.7   (a) Battleship Rock, New Mexico: an outlier of an ignimbrite flow from the Valles Caldera. [G. Fielder]. (b) Location of Battleship Rock (lower left corner) in relation to the Valles Caldera (top). [G. Fielder]. (c) This is a detail of the welded part of the ignimbrite, seen in Fig. 18.7(a) immediately below the non-welded top, showing that, like aerofoils, the blunt ends of fiammées point upstream. [G. Fielder]

FIGURE 18.8   Note the hexagonal shape of this large lunar crater, Ptolemaeus, 164 km diameter. [From the Photographic Lunar Atlas, Plate D5e (P), in Gerard P. Kuiper (Eds.), © The University of Chicago, courtesy UC Press]

FIGURE 18.9   Saturation cratering on the lunar farside: a photograph taken in 1972 by astronaut K. Mattingly from Apollo 16 in orbit. The crater, with central mountains, near to the top left is Lobachevsky (84km diameter). Further south the crater King (76 km) has a complex central eminence. [Apollo 16, NASA]

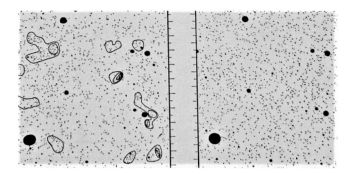

FIGURE 18.10   In this example of a dot map, each dot represents the centre of an observed crater. Larger craters are shown in black. [G. Fielder]

analysis showed that, between the selenographic longitudes +20° and –20° the number density increased as the latitude decreased from 60° to 0°. In other words, in the central portions of the nearside, there are more craters per unit of surface, as the equator of the Moon is approached, than expected on the assumption that the craters are all of random impact origin. I had already found[33] a similar result (Fig. 18.11) for bright craters, catalogued by D. Ettenfield. These craters, smaller than 20 km across, would form a single population. I would have expected them to be recent impact craters, because the surface rocks in and around such craters could have whitened, relative to the surrounding rocks, as a result of crushing. However, the observations indicated a

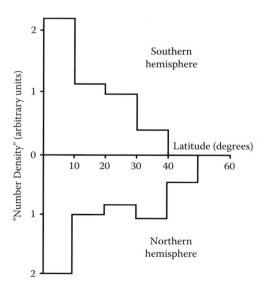

FIGURE 18.11   Histogram showing the unexpected distributions of craters in the central portions of the near side of the Moon. [G. Fielder]

dependence of number density on latitude. Taken together, both analyses (counts in dark terrain in the central meridional region and counts of bright craters over a wider zone) show a distinct concentration of craters towards the equator in the central parts of the Moon's near side. These non-random distributions of smallish craters may be understood if a significant number of them is of endogenic origin.

The Proportion of Endocraters to Impact Craters

19

In itself, that result is of interest; but the procedure does not reveal the actual proportion of endocraters in a given area. The prepared dot maps, representing crater centres, were examined, in turn, through square blocks of five equal area strips inscribed on clear acetate (as in Fig. 11.1). The centre of each block was placed, in sequence, in each of ten random positions, starting with the length of a strip placed parallel to a north-bearing line marked on each map. The number of dots that fell within each of the strips was counted. The block was then turned about its centre in increments of 10° of azimuth, up to 170°, and the counting procedure repeated. The actual dimensions of a strip, five times longer than its width, were set for each area under test by involving the total number of crater centres in that area. In that way, we were able to allocate an average of five dots per strip; and that ensured high sensitivity and reliability of the tests. From the counts, we evaluated the "index of dispersion" of each set of data: this method gave information on both chaining and clustering of craters.

In order to embrace our further requirement – that of discovering the probable percentage of each type of small crater in each of our selected areas – it was necessary to involve additional computer testing on known distributions of crater centres. To this end, Fryer was able to use the CDC computer of the University of Arizona. He performed tests on two-dimensional arrays of points consisting of a constant number of points in a fixed area but with a known fraction of these points distributed randomly and the remaining fraction, P, aligned parallel to a given azimuth in the same area.

The points forming the first, linear chain were allocated a constant mutual separation and the index of dispersion, V, calculated for that test area. Parallel chains with the same separation between points were added and V was re-calculated for successive cases in which P was increased until all the points in the area were arranged in parallel chains. Tests were then run with different separations between the points that represented chains of craters. The index V was calculated for all these cases. Diagrams of V plotted against the azimuthal angle, α, of the block of parallel lines were prepared for each of the 41 mare-type areas studied, in our original paper[35]; and Fig. 19.1 shows the corresponding mean values drawn from all these areas. We also prepared diagrams that relate V to the separations between craters in chains for various values of P (the proportions of craters in chains).

DOI: 10.1201/9781003181279-19

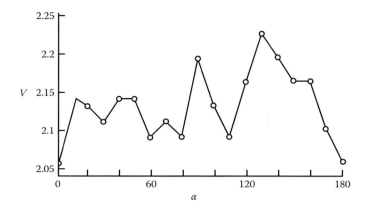

FIGURE 19.1   V-alpha diagram showing the mean values of V versus azimuth of all 41 mare-type areas studied. [G. Fielder]

The method of finding the proportion of real (lunar) craters in chains, for any particular azimuth, may best be explained by reference to an idealised V-α diagram (Fig. 19.2) that separates those craters that are clustered from those that occur in chains. By considering parallelism of crater chains over large areas, we effectively eliminated secondary impact crater chains, since they would not exhibit parallelism over our chosen, large areas; and we, therefore, regarded the crater chains as being fracture controlled.

In Fig. 19.2, the level V = 0 identifies a regular, or uniform, distribution of craters and the level V=1 corresponds to a random distribution of craters. Commonly, our plots of V against α lie at a level of V that is > 1. Peaks of V that lie at, or below, V = 1.74 (the 0.001% level of significance) are rejected in our quest to find the proportion of craters in chains. A first conclusion from the tests for V is that the majority of craters that measure from 100 m to a few km in diameter are non-randomly distributed. This general result was found, also, from independent photometric and square-counting methods. The non-randomness is exhibited as clustering and chaining of craters.

Surprisingly, special tests, that involved three fields of random points on which artificial, dense clusters of points were superimposed, proved that compact clusters of craters that are easily recognized by eye had little effect in raising the V-value of a random distribution above unity. The values of V where such condensed clustering occurs are shown by the stippling in Fig. 19.2. The raising of V to the levels above the region of condensed clustering depends, largely, on more general, diffuse clustering that is less obvious to the eye.

One possible cause of these fluctuations in the number-density of craters is to be found in lava flows that cover a part, or parts, of an area under investigation. For example, some wrinkle ridges have, apparently, extruded lavas that flowed away from one side of the ridge but not from the other side. In these cases, number densities of craters might differ from one side to the other.

Peaks in V over its general level are due, also, to the alignments of craters in the directions specified on the V – α diagram. For each test area, the level V_{av} represents

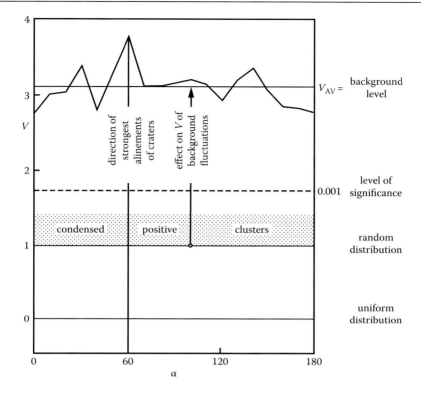

FIGURE 19.2 Schematic idealised V-alpha diagram. [G. Fielder]

the mean value of V for all 18 values of α. Above that level, the proportion of craters in chains can be estimated for any azimuth, a high peak in V, for a given area, revealing the direction of a strong alignment of craters in that area.

Studying our 41 mare-type areas, most of which were on the near side of the Moon (because of the scarcity of mare-type areas on the far side) we confirmed that there were wide variations in the type of crater, as well as in the number-densities of craters, between individual areas. Our best (weighted) estimates of the averaged, total proportion of internally formed craters are from 33% to 51%. Some individual areas of Oceanus Procellarum and Mare Frigoris (shown to the north of the dark-floored crater Plato in Fig. 1.1) have yielded maxima proportions of clustering that exceed 80% and maxima proportions of linear chaining that approach 30%. In these regions, many of the clustered craters could be a mix of endo- and exo-genic craters. Virtually all the chained craters are considered to be endo craters, for reasons given in Section 20.

On the other hand, in areas such as parts of Mare Humorum, the dark floor of Tsiolkovski (on the lunar farside) and an area in Sinus Medii, both the clustering and the chaining reach only about 14%. Evidently, the number of endocraters per unit of mare-type surface varies greatly from place to place. If attempting to date any part of the lunar surface using crater counts, it is vital, therefore, to distinguish between craters of different geneses.

The Origin of Crater - Chains in Grid Fractures

20

Most of our study areas are distributed around the equatorial belt of the Moon. The peaks in Fig. 19.1 lie at position angles (measured eastwards from north) of 130°, corresponding to my system A (the most strongly developed system of lineaments on the near side of the Moon), 130° to 160° (system R_i, sub-radial to Mare Imbrium), 90° (the least conspicuous system, D, of lineaments), 40° to 50° (system B), and 8° (close to the peak direction of system C).

The highest peak in Fig. 19.1 occurs at $\alpha = 130°$ and broadens to cover precisely the range of azimuth that is occupied by the most conspicuous lineaments that are associated with Mare Imbrium. The 90° peak was unexpected because it corresponded to my system D, running E–W in equatorial regions, where I found few lineaments and thought that the reason was that this direction was one in which lineaments might not be seen easily since, bearing in mind the position of the Sun, they could cast only short shadows (if any). However, craters in chains that run E–W will, of course, cast shadows; these might have been the features that our method picked out. On a point of caution, it should be noted that the majority of the individual framelets of the Lunar Orbiter photographs were joined along the direction $\alpha = 90°$, so we questioned the reality of the 90° peak in Fig. 19.1; but checks on other Lunar Orbiter photographs that had framelets inclined to the 90° direction by up to 20° did, in fact, show chaining in the E–W direction.

Overall, the peaks of V show a remarkably strong correlation between the mapped trends of chains of small craters and the directions of the deduced fractures of the grid system. This finding strongly reinforces our contention that the majority of these craters in chains are endogenic.

In the foregoing discussion of the distribution of craters in maria, we reasoned that lava flows, covering some areas of the surface and not others, were one possible cause of the contrasts in the number densities of craters across each study area. Unknown to us at the time of our counts, one of those study areas happened to cover parts of the now well-known, late flows in Mare Imbrium (see Fig. 21.1). Considering the whole of the study area, we found clustering that ranged from 20% to 30% but, when the area was sub-divided, we found clustering of only 10% to 20% in the north-eastern half and appreciably higher clustering of 28% to 32% in the south-western half of the area. It

DOI: 10.1201/9781003181279-20

97

was in this south-western area that the best- developed flow fronts, together with several wrinkle ridges, were in evidence. This observation serves to confirm our contention that successive lava flows in maria may well have contributed to the clustering of craters. Consequently, in order to avoid this effect on clustering, it is necessary to examine the distribution of craters within the bounds of each discrete lava flow.

The Origins of Small Craters in a **21** Lunar Lava Flow

An older lunar surface might be expected to accrue more damage, from the on-going rain of meteoroids now observed in the vicinity of the Earth and Moon, than a younger surface close to it. So an older lava flow might be expected to sport more impact craters, per unit area, than a younger, superimposed lava flow. Yet, when I was first shown a high-resolution Lunar Orbiter 5 photograph (Fig. 21.1) of some of the flood basalts in Mare Imbrium, I was amazed to note that a stratigraphically higher (and, therefore, later) flow appeared to carry appreciably more craters than were present in an equivalent area of the older, adjacent terrain. This unexpected situation led me to describe a quite separate method of establishing the presence of genetically mixed craters on the Moon. Also, an independent estimate of the respective percentages of the craters that were of endogenic, and exogenic, origin could be made.

The Boeing Aircraft Corporation had designed and built five Lunar Orbiter spacecraft for NASA. These missions were placed in a succession of orbits around the Moon. The original image data had been transmitted from each spacecraft following a special, on-board development process and Boeing held the prime data at their laboratories in Seattle, including some imagery that was not generally available to the public. So when, in August 1968, J. Noyes, Head of the Geo-astrophysics Laboratory, offered me a Consultancy at the Boeing Scientific Research Laboratories I drove to Seattle with my family, keen to extract all that I could about the craters on those intriguing lava flows in Mare Imbrium.

If a bottle of tomato ketchup is shaken and then poured on a smooth, inclined board, the ketchup can be seen to form a lobate flow front. Basalts, returned from the Moon by the Apollo astronauts, are fine-grained volcanic rocks that are relatively poor in silica. When basalts are fluidised by heating them to temperatures in excess of 1000°C, they behave in similar fashion to ketchup. Basalt flows in Hawaii were shown in Fig. 18.6. On the Moon, low viscosity lunar flood-basalts were erupted, at first probably from fissures or, possibly, from low shields that are now concealed by lavas, and later flows travelled for several hundreds of kilometres across the lunar surface (Fig. 21.2). Samples of mare lavas returned through the Apollo programme and melted in the laboratory have even lower viscosities than their terrestrial counterparts. In an

DOI: 10.1201/9781003181279-21

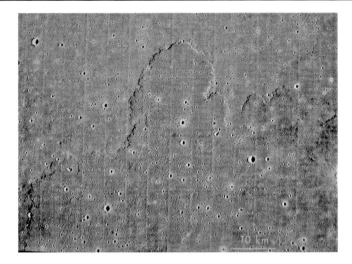

FIGURE 21.1   A late lava flow, in Mare Imbrium, studied by the author. [Lunar Orbiter 5, NASA]

FIGURE 21.2   Lava flows, with channels, to the west of the eminence La Hire, in Mare Imbrium. [Apollo 15, NASA]

extensive photogeological search for the sources of the last flows in Mare Imbrium, my Research Student R. Todhunter[71] identified fissures, cones and craters, as well as a downfaulted block of mare terrain (Fig. 21.3), to the south-west of Euler (27 km in diameter) in Mare Imbrium.

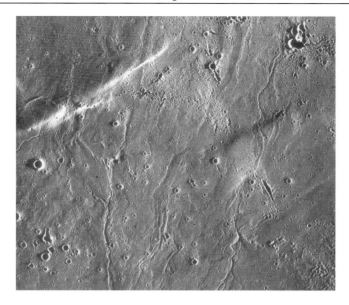

FIGURE 21.3 A probable downfaulted block SW of Euler, Mare Imbrium. [Apollo 15, NASA]

Flow thicknesses vary: I measured the shadows cast at various points along the front of the flow f2 in Mare Imbrium (Fig. 21.1) and estimated the mean flow thickness there to be > 23 m. Fig 21.4(a) shows a ground view of the front of a congealed terrestrial lava flow. A similar, but active flow front is shown in Fig. 21.4(b).

In the case of terrestrial lava flows, craters frequently form by collapse (Fig. 21.5b) of the surface layers into underlying tubes (Fig. 21.5a) along which liquid lava once

(a)   (b)

FIGURE 21.4 (a) Jane Fielder standing next to a static front of basaltic lava in the Pinacate region of Mexico. [G. Fielder]. (b) An active lava front, contributing to the formation of the Icelandic island of Surtsey, photographed on 28 February, 1965 as it enters the sea. [Sigurdur Thorarinsson]

(a)

(b)

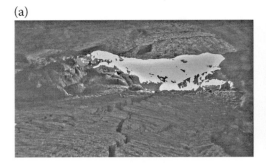

FIGURE 21.5 (a) Interior of a drained lava tube on the flanks of Mauna Loa, Hawaii. [G.Fielder]. (b) A lava crust that has collapsed into a lava tube, Mauna Loa. On the Moon, draining of regolith under gravity could leave a shallow channel in the surface. [G. Fielder]

streamed; so I looked for any similar features on the Moon. Examining the lunar flows f1 and f2, shown in Fig. 21.6, I found some short crater chains on f1 and more numerous chains on f2. Because of their observed directions, these chains appeared to be tectonically controlled. A possible mechanism might be demonstrated by my photograph (Fig. 18.1) of a wedge-shaped lava rising along a fracture and prising it open; except that, on the Moon, the wedge shape would not remain when close to the surface, because the rising lava would disperse through the sudden drop of pressure and its likely explosive volatility. However, I also found shallow channels (Fig. 21.6) in the covering of regolith. The channels tended to fan out towards the best developed flow fronts; and it seemed evident that regolith had drained into subterranean tubes. The presence of flow units – lavas that had burst through a congealing lava front – were also noted and were spaced at intervals along the principal flow front of f2 (Fig. 21.6).

Because of the lack of atmospheric pressure on the Moon, any gas-rich lava approaching the surface of a lunar flow would outgas explosively and expand adiabatically (a process in which the temperature of the lava falls). Radiative heat loss would occur and, in dispersing, the lava would freeze. Our early laboratory experiments, in which L. Wilson and I simulated freshly erupted lunar lavas, showed that this mechanism, specific to the Moon, would have created a froth of highly porous lava (Fig 16.2) that would act as an excellent thermal insulator of the underlying lavas. Basaltic froth, freezing in the low lunar gravity field ($^1/_6$ the strength of Earth's) could lead to a thicker regolith roof, above a liquid lava, than in the case of the roof above a tube of chemically identical lava on the Earth.

The immediately obvious distinction between the crater densities on the respective flows f1 and f2 (Fig. 21.7) needed to be quantified. Working with templates inscribed on clear acetate, my wife Jane was able to measure the diameters of some 7000 craters on large photo-prints specially prepared by Boeing. (She worked during the times when our baby daughter Clare was taking her regular daily nap!) At the same time, I made counts of differently sized craters using the medium resolution coverage of the flows - the areas marked M in Fig. 21.6. We found that craters between 333 m and 1000 m in diameter (Δ) were more than twice as numerous in the later (stratigraphically higher) flow, f2, than in the earlier flow, f1. (See count areas M1 and M2 in Table 21.1.)

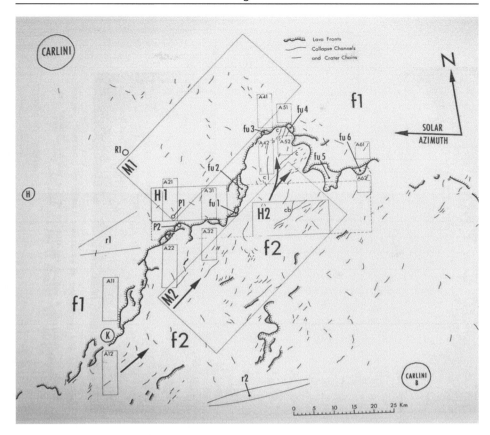

FIGURE 21.6 Sketch of the flow shown in Fig. 21.1 depicting (a) the main lava fronts; (b) channels and crater-chains; (c) the positions of six flow units marked fu 1, fu 2, ... fu 6; and (d) the locations of the rectangular areas on the flows f1 and f2 where special crater counts were made. [R. Strom and G. Fielder[40]]

To investigate the possibility that any large explosion craters in, or in the vicinity of, f2, might have ejected materials that created secondary impact craters in f2, further counts were completed in sample areas of six pairs of strips labelled A in Fig. 21.6. Each pair, A11, A12; A21, A22; ... to A61, A62 was located near to the flow front of f2, the first strip of each pair being on f1 and the second, facing the first, on f2. Counts in each strip area included craters as small as 50 m across in the size bracket 50 m to 225 m. Size brackets of 225 m to 333 m and 333 m to 500 m were also covered. The counts of craters in this last size bracket could be compared (Table 21.1) with the counts taken from the medium resolution coverage (M).

Both sets of counts showed more craters in f2 than in f1. By contrast, it is seen, in Table 21.1, that, for the crater size range 50 m to 225 m (sample area A) and 160 m to 225 m (area H), these smallest craters counted are essentially equal in number density in f1 and in f2. Finally, high resolution (H) counts in the size brackets 333 m to 500 m,

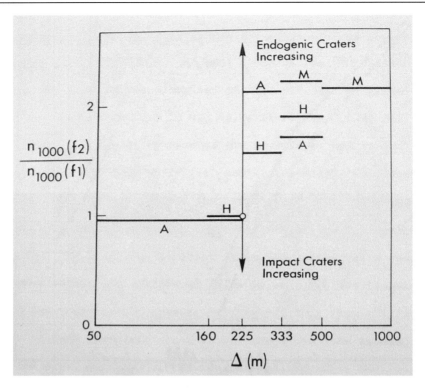

FIGURE 21.7   The number of craters, in the specified ranges of size (Δ), per 1000 km^2 of surface on the flow f2 (see Fig. 21.6) compared with the number of craters per 1000 km^2 of surface on the flow f1, given separately for the respective areas A, M and H (Fig. 21.6). Clearly, there are many more of the larger craters, found to the right of the vertical line, on f2 than on f1. This establishes a strong contribution from internally formed craters on the later flow f2. [G. Fielder]

225 m to 333 m, and 160 m to 225 m provide further evidence for both the discrepancy of the larger craters between the units f1 and f2 and the equality of number densities in the case of the smaller craters up to 225 m in diameter. The craters smaller than 225 m, in both flows, may well represent impact craters, or mixed groups of impact and endocraters.

These counts prove that there is an abrupt increase in the number densities of craters that are larger than 225 m in diameter as the boundary between f1 and f2 is crossed. This discontinuity in the number density of craters is tied to the mapped fronts of f2. Thus, the effects (if any) of secondary cratering on our counts must be very small; and the 50% excess of craters on the flow f2 must represent predominantly endogenic craters. Many of these results were originally reported in a Boeing Document[37], parts of which are reproduced elsewhere.[30]

Of the remaining craters in f2, it is not so easy to say what proportion of each type of crater might be present. A problem is that craters formed internally by explosive gas

TABLE 21.1 CRATER COUNTS IN FLOWS

COUNTS OF CRATERS IN f2		COUNTS OF CRATERS IN f1	
Count area M2		Count area M1	
Diam.(m)	n_{1000}	Diam.(m)	n_{1000}
333–500	208	333–500	94
500–1000	30	500–1000	14
Count area A2		Count area A1	
Diam.(m)	n_{1000}	Diam.(m)	n_{1000}
50–225	14630	50–225	15270
333–500	177	333–500	104
Count area H2		Count area H1	
Diam.(m)	n_{1000}	Diam.(m)	n_{1000}
160–225	1546	160–225	1563
225–333	312	225–333	200
333–500	98	333–500	52

Note: n_{1000} is the number of craters per 1000 km^2 of count area.

emissions through the regolith could present essentially those characteristics that we expect to see in eumorphics formed by impact; although it is true to say that most of the craters that appear in f2 differ, in morphology, from that expected in the case of recent impact craters. Drainage of regolith might be involved in altering the shapes of craters formed internally but not so much in energetic impacts that penetrate deeper into underlying rocks. There is room for some detailed morphological studies of the craters in f2.

Small Double Craters

22

Although relatively few among the craters identified, possible impact craters are those circular craters that show sharp features such as an upturned rim that casts a thin crescent of shadow outside the crater as well as a relatively sharply defined internal shadow. I have referred to these as eumorphic craters. The largest are surrounded by bright haloes and, mapping them on the high resolution (H) coverage, we noticed that many were double, a smaller crater nesting (most frequently concentrically) within the larger one. These eumorphics are found in roughly equal numbers per unit area (see Table 22.1) on both of the flows f1 and f2. There is a strong possibility that many of them are impact craters.

I was able to use an "original" Boeing medium resolution negative to look for and count bright halo craters that measured > 200 km in diameter in areas M1 and M2 of Fig. 21.6. The counts are given in Table 22.2 and the numbers of craters in each, equal area were comparable. The craters themselves appeared to be randomly distributed and a few, in each area, contained blocks. There were 14 of these bright halo craters per 1000 km^2. It will be seen, from Tables 22.1 and 22.2, that the numbers of eumorphic and bright halo craters per 1000 km^2 of terrain increase with diminishing size of crater, as expected from impact frequency laws.

The Apollo seismometers have proved that some natural impacts are occurring on the Moon at present. Expectations are that many small impacts have occurred in all regions of the Moon, including at times that post-date the emplacement of the lava flows under study. It might seem realistic, therefore, to categorise most of the eumorphic craters as impact craters. Although random impacts would be expected to produce more craters in the older, f1, unit, the observed rough equality between the numbers of eumorphic craters in the areas H1 and H2 (see Table 22.1) might mean that the flows f1 and f2 were emplaced within the same, short interval of time.

TABLE 22.1 Eumorphic craters in areas H

CRATER DIAMETER (m)	NO. IN H1	NO. IN H2	n_{1000}
55-75	18	20	106
77-110	15	12	75
113-205	3	5	22

DOI: 10.1201/9781003181279-22

TABLE 22.2   Bright halo craters with diameters exceeding 200 km

TOTAL NUMBER PER 1000 km^2 = 14	
NO. IN M1	*NO. IN M2*
16	13
(5 with blocks)	(3 with blocks)

Most of the eumorphic craters noted in Table 22.1 are smaller than 110 m in diameter. Bearing in mind that the numbers listed in Table 22.1 are small, we found that 70% of them, in both f1 and f2, are double. In f1, they have shallow, inner craters but, in f2, the inner craters are deep. At the time when these assessments were made, up to $^2/_3$ of the diameters of the inner craters in f2 were covered with shadow. Of the double craters, 58% of them in f1 contain central blocks. By contrast, blocks are found in only 8% of the double craters in f2.

Double Craters and the Depth and Compaction of the Regolith

23

The cross-section of a double crater is sketched in Fig. 23.1. All of the double craters have an internal bench, or terrace, which I estimated to be at an average depth of 5.7 m below the rim. The depth of the bench varies little with the size and location (f1 or f2) of the crater. I reason that these benches are indicative of the depth of regolith, so both flows appear to be covered by the same depth of detritus. However, the regolith of f2 (the later flow, with the clearly developed flow front) covers lava that appears to offer lower resistance to an incoming projectile than does the lava of f1. That might explain how a missile would plummet through the less compact regolith of f2 and then penetrate the lava beneath, creating an inner crater in the process; whilst the older, possibly more compact, lavas of f1 might serve to preserve parts of the missile as blocks of rock. An alternative theory is that the lavas of f1 and f2 differ in physical structure or in composition. Flow ridging, common on some lava flows, including some flows on the Moon that are much later than those discussed here, would probably not be seen on flows that are covered with regolith.

The double craters bear a striking resemblance to the experimental impact craters of Oberbeck and Quaide, formed in two-layered media in which the lower layer is

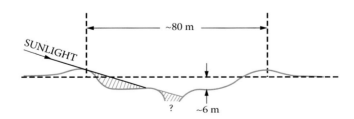

FIGURE 23.1 Proposed vertical cross-section through the centre of a double (concentric) crater, sketched approximately to scale. Note the bench at a depth of about 6 m and the inner crater that is covered by about 2/3 of its rim-diameter with shadow. [G. Fielder]

DOI: 10.1201/9781003181279-23

more strongly bonded than the upper layer[38]. Blocks of rock are commonly present in low-velocity, secondary impact craters produced by ejecta from terrestrial explosion craters. In the case of terrestrial flows of basalt, the depths of in-flow craters that are caused by collapse approximate, or are less than, the thicknesses of the flows. The same is probably true for the craters larger than 225 m on the lunar flow f2.

Dating the Mare Flows

24

Although the flow f2 has not been dated, other lavas from a site in Oceanus Procellarum not far from the possible source region[71] of the lavas f1 and f2 have been returned to Earth and dated. The youngest are 3.1×10^9 years old. Even the flow f2, which is stratigraphically high in the Moon sequence of layering, is likely to be little younger than that. Yet it is evident that erosional and denudational forces have not led to the degradation of the flow front of f2 to anything near to the extent required to render it unrecognisable in that time interval. To wear down a crater wall by 10 m every 10^9 years, for example, might be possible in theory – especially with any increased flux of incoming meteoroids over that of the present day – but it would probably need to involve, also, a lateral transportation mechanism such as moonquakes aiding the creep of detritus under gravity.

I am driven to propose that there might remain the possibility that the submorphic craters in f2 are not to be regarded as denuded eumorphic craters: possibly, a high proportion of the submorphics have been in the submorphic class from their birth. How else would a flow that generated so many endocraters in a one-off process, when it was forming, remain, along with its frozen showcase, for up to 3×10^9 years?

Table 24.1, derived from the data in Table 21.1, lists the minimum numbers of endocraters per 1000 km^2 in the flow f2 and is based on the excess of craters in f2 over the counts of craters in f1. The minimum percentages of internally formed craters given in Table 24.1 may now be compared with the result obtained from the index of dispersion tests on the area of Mare Imbrium that covers the flows f1 and f2. These index of dispersion tests point to an average percentage of endocraters[37] stretching over the range 34% to 64%. In fact, that range satisfactorily brackets all the minima percentages of endocraters in the flow f2 that are given in the last column of Table 24.1.

There remains the problem of all the other craters on the flows. Why should f2 carry more endocraters than f1? I would have thought that to be unlikely when the flows were first formed. Of course, compositional differences between the flows are quite possible, so the degree of outgassing might have differed between them. Nevertheless, I would not expect the older flow, f1, to carry no endocraters at all. And I would expect to find some endocraters among the craters left unaccounted for in f2. Our tests were capable of revealing only minima in the numbers of endocraters. There could be a whole lot more internally formed craters than we have been able to assess.

More detailed morphological studies of all the remaining craters in our study areas might, possibly, provide answers to these questions. For example, my assistant J. Murray

TABLE 24.1   Endocraters in the flow f2

CRATER DIAMETER (m)	SAMPLE AREA (km²)	MIN. NO. PER 1000 km²	MIN. %-AGE OF ENDOCRATERS ON f2
500–1000	M 1030	16	54
333–500	M 1030	114	55
333–500	H 180	46	50
333–500	A* 190	73	41
225–333	H 180	112	38
225–333	A* 190	327	52

* Area found by the addition of all six areas A on the flow f2.

used circular and elliptical templates to compare the shapes of 234 craters in the flows f1 and f2. He found that, in f2, circular craters outnumbered elliptical craters whereas, in f1, elliptical craters outnumbered circular ones. Perhaps there will be another manned mission to Mare Imbrium, this time to examine the specific flows discussed here.

To sum up, small lunar craters are decisively non-randomly distributed in the mare type areas and probably (from the smaller data sets that I have noted earlier) elsewhere, too. At least part of the reason for the clustering of craters in maria is to be found in the presence of discrete flows of lava. Other non-randomness is found in the chains of craters that trend, through the maria, in sympathy with the directions of underlying fractures: for reasons given in the foregoing account these chains, many not previously noticed, must be essentially of internal origin.

The numbers of internally formed craters vary greatly across the dark areas. In general, the percentage of these endocraters exceeds 33% and, allowing for craters not classified into types, is possibly much more than 50% of the total number of craters in specific mare regions. Among fine lineaments, chains of small craters that parallel other lineaments are, most probably, entirely of endocraters.

Craters that are crisply defined and circular, especially those that display, in addition, bright haloes and that tend to be randomly disposed as well as having equal number-densities in adjacent areas, are the most probable candidates for the small impact crater category that must be present on the Moon. Those that are nested, and that contain blocks of rock or deep dimples, are also likely to be exogenic.

Studies of Large Craters

25

Because the numbers of craters on the Moon decrease with increasing size of crater, it is not possible to complete meaningful statistical analyses on the largest craters in the manner that I have done for the small craters. However, other approaches that use statistical treatments to elucidate the origins of some of the larger craters have been attempted. Some statistical data that relate to the near side of the Moon will be found in my books "Lunar Geology" [21] (which discusses the distribution of the larger craters in the lunar highlands as well as in the maria) and "Structure of the Moon's Surface" [67] (which reports some early work on the statistics of craters). More recently W. Elston noticed that, over both the near and the far sides of the Moon, for all mutually intersecting pairs of craters larger than 10 km in diameter, the vectors that can be drawn from the centre of the older crater to the centre of the crater that is overlapping it are non-random in direction. Vectors that are directed eastwards were found to dominate on the near-side of the Moon, whereas vectors directed to the west were found to dominate on the far-side. With his associates, Elston et al.[77] suggested that these craters were all volcanic ring structures and that the younger crater of each pair had migrated in a direction possibly controlled by a convective process in the body of the Moon.

By contrast, Spurr[4] followed traditional geological methods in his attempts to elucidate the origins of large lunar craters and he grouped the craters into types. One of these types was his "graben-crater", examples being Ptolemaeus (Fig. 18.8) and Clavius (Fig. 43.2). Noting that graben craters had polygonal shapes, Spurr reasoned that they grew from deep-seated fissures or fractures: he observed that chains of graben craters tended to be rectilinear and that, commonly, the chains ran in directions close to those of meridians. This direction of fracturing is common to that found by Gash and me, in our analysis of rotational and tidal stressing.

Although I have some empathy with Spurr's methods, the majority of lunar students would, I gather, dismiss Spurr's purely geological reasoning. Most would argue emphatically that the largest craters were all of impact origin. However, like Spurr, I think that studies of the large lunar craters should indeed centre on the details of their morphologies as well as on their interrelationships; but, until the space age led to high-resolution images of the Moon's surface, it was difficult to access the level of detail required to uncover the critical facts needed in geomorphological studies of the origins of large lunar craters. That has now changed; and some clear results will be found in the following discussion.

The Ray-Craters Tycho, Copernicus and Aristarchus

26

At full Moon, the bright rays that diverge from Tycho, 102 km in diameter (see Fig. 1.1), Copernicus (93 km, Fig. 26.1), Aristarchus (40 km, Fig. 26.2) and other craters, are an impressive sight. The rays traverse all types of lunar topographic feature as multiple, bright streaks. Tycho's rays are exceptionally long: one of them might be as long as 1900 km but the habit the rays have of dispersing and becoming difficult to track at large distances from the crater makes this estimate unreliable. A few of the major rays of Tycho are tangential to its walls; but the rays are composed of short "ray elements" that, taken individually, point roughly towards the centre of the crater or its floor[70]. This property of rays can be seen more clearly in some of the rays of Copernicus (Fig. 26.3). Many of the ray elements result from the forward throwout from secondary impact craters caused by the oblique impacts of ejecta from the primary crater. Some rays, or parts of them, coincide with topographic ridges and walls of craters (small and large); or they might confuse with the normal brightness of highland-type ridges or some chains of craters; but, in general, the alignments of long rays and of ray-elements show little preference to the directions of the A and B families of the lunar grid system.

An irregular, dark grey collar, or halo, surrounds the crater Tycho (Fig. 26.4). Some other craters (for example, Mairan) display similar features. The crater Pictet, 62 km in diameter, lies, within the dark halo, immediately to the east of Tycho and gives a measure of the general width of the halo. In 1911, Miethe and Seegert[39] used UV and orange spectral passbands to secure useful colour images of the Moon which showed that Tycho's dark halo reflected less UV than orange light. Some acidic rocks (granite, rhyolite and pitchstone), the intermediate rock trachyte and the basic rock augite absorb the UV, while even small quantities of sulphur absorb the UV strongly. Surveyor VII soft-landed within the dark halo on an early flow - possibly a base surge from the Tycho impact - beyond the north rim of Tycho and found the rocks there to be anorthositic. However, lakes of dark lavas (Fig. 26.5) are common in and around the walls of both Tycho and Aristarchus and are almost certainly a cause of some of the dark patches and bands seen, under high light, in the inner ringwall terraces of Aristarchus (Fig. 26.6). Possibly, patches of dark lava that have been sheltered from the ray-forming missiles contribute to the tone of the Tycho halo. Again, the dark haloes of craters do seem to

DOI: 10.1201/9781003181279-26

FIGURE 26.1 The rays of Copernicus. [Adapted from E. Whitaker et al., Rectified Lunar Atlas, University of Arizona Press (1963), Plate 12d (W)]

FIGURE 26.2 The rays of Aristarchus. [Adapted from E. Whitaker et al., Rectified Lunar Atlas, University of Arizona Press (1963), Plate 11c (Y)]

FIGURE 26.3 Some of the ray-elements of Copernicus. The short, white streaks of ray-elements are best seen to the SW, and to the N, of Copernicus. [Adapted from E. Whitaker et al., Rectified Lunar Atlas, University of Arizona Press, 1963, Plate 12c (Y)]

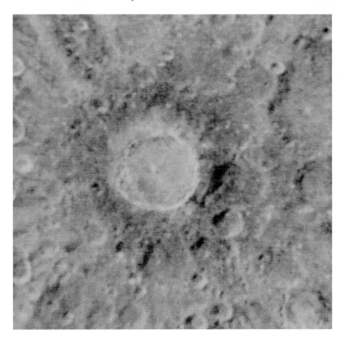

FIGURE 26.4 The dark halo that surrounds Tycho. [Adapted from E. Whitaker et al., Rectified Lunar Atlas, University of Arizona Press (1963), Plate 24c (Y)]

FIGURE 26.5   Dark lakes, thought to be of lava, marked A and B, together with a flow f, sited in the north wall of Aristarchus. It seems that liquid lavas were extruded from fractures and tended to level depressions. [Lunar Orbiter V, NASA]

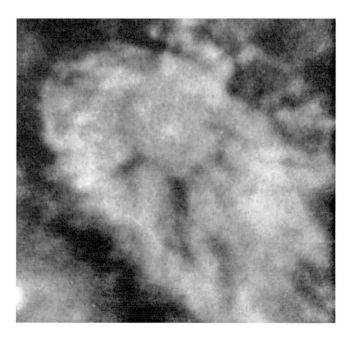

FIGURE 26.6   In the inner walls of Aristarchus, patches of dark lava that are recognised, under high resolution and with low lighting, as flows and lakes meld under high lighting at lower resolution to give the appearance of dark bands. [From Strom and Fielder][40]

FIGURE 26.7 Tycho (diameter 102 km). [Lunar Orbiter V, NASA]

coincide with the zones of plastic deformation that are to be expected around some impact craters, as revealed by my analysis of crater deltoids[82]. Other possible causes might involve heating and chemical changes.

Although the eye sees the rays as white, even the brightest ray-centre, Aristarchus, reflects only 20% of the light that falls on it. That is similar to the reflectivity of volcanic ash and can be compared to the 7% general reflectivity of the Moon's near-side. Finding a model that matches the light-scattering properties of the rays at all phases of the Moon is not easy[32]; but the best model would probably involve disturbed deposits, including regolith, particulates and blocks of rock, together with negative topography that includes small craters.

In comparison with most other craters of their size, the walls of Tycho (Fig. 26.7) and Copernicus are quite cleanly sculptured. Together with the evidence from the rays, which requires high energies of ejection and adds to the requirement that the parent craters are high in the stratigraphic column, these craters must, I think, be among the last large craters to be formed on the Moon. Tycho itself is, in fact, widely regarded as symbolic of a recent, large impact crater.

Unexpected Volcanic Flows in Tycho and Aristarchus

27

In the summer of 1967, Lunar Orbiter spacecraft – and especially Lunar Orbiter 5 – delivered much of the important material that was needed to investigate the processes of formation of large lunar craters; and, the next year, I had the privilege of working at the University of Arizona's Lunar and Planetary Laboratory on the excellent imagery of Tycho and Aristarchus acquired by that U.S. mission.

R. Strom and I were able to examine medium resolution coverage down to about 40m showing both Tycho (Fig. 26.7) and Aristarchus, as well as high resolution images of parts of Tycho and all of Aristarchus in which details as small as 5 m were revealed. Immediately, many flow features (Figs. 27.1 and 27.2) were found in, and close to, the walls of both craters. That was a big surprise to us. Characterized by their similarities to lava flows on the Earth, these lunar flows were undoubtedly of lava.

Arcuate flow ridging (Fig. 27.3), caused by the frictional drag of liquid lava flowing underneath a cooling, congealing crust of lava, flow channels (Fig. 27.1) with leveées (raised edges caused by the successive spillover of cooling lavas) and bulbous lava fronts were all present, enabling the directions of past flows to be deduced and the nature of the flows to be evaluated. Strom was able to discover a number of source craters from which some of the flows had been extruded (Fig. 27.2). In that process he had revealed one kind of small volcanic crater on the Moon. The geometry of the flows and the details of the flow ridging proved that, when the lavas were erupted, they were appreciably more viscous than the lavas that flowed towards and across Mare Imbrium: because of the low viscosity of the mare flows they were able to travel distances of hundreds of kilometers. By contrast, the longest flows in and around Tycho flowed only tens of kilometers before solidifying.

Our investigations of the volcanism in the northern parts of Tycho were restricted to the coverage available on the high-resolution imagery. Also when Lunar Orbiter 5 photographed Tycho, the shadows cast by its eastern wall covered much of the inner wall and floor detail; but we were able to use the medium resolution images to find other lava flows in the southern parts of the inner, terraced walls. The lavas that were

DOI: 10.1201/9781003181279-27

FIGURE 27.1   Flow channels with levées beyond the crest of Tycho's northern wall. [Lunar Orbiter V, NASA]

FIGURE 27.2   Flows outside the northern wall crest of Aristarchus, with two of the lava sources marked at L and C. [Lunar Orbiter V, NASA]

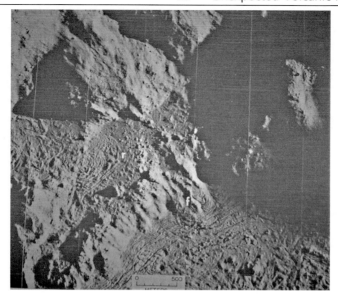

FIGURE 27.3   Arcuate flow ridging at **r** in the inner wall of Tycho, showing the direction of flow. Note also the levéed channels, containing the flow that reaches the lava floor of Tycho and terminates in a characteristically bulbous front at **f**. The scale shows up to 500m [Lunar Orbiter V, NASA]

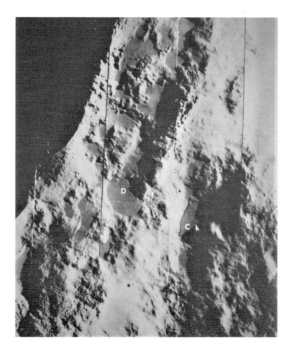

FIGURE 27.4   Several lava lakes, two of them marked **C** and **D**, in the SE rim of Tycho. [Lunar Orbiter V, NASA]

erupted from sources in the northern and southern walls of Tycho might have been assisted, in their ascent, by the presence of the north-to-south running fractures discussed earlier. We did not find any major flows to the east and west sides of Tycho but Strom[30] did discover many lava lakes (Fig. 27.4) set in the (mainly eastern) outer walls.

Volcanic Tumuli on the Floor of Tycho

28

Details in the north-western part of Tycho's floor were ideally illuminated for our investigations. Far from showing a little-modified impact crater, the high-resolution pictures of the floor presented a strikingly unambiguous view of an extensive lava field (Fig. 28.1). These lavas had formed numerous tumular hills, mostly elongate in shape, the largest of them up to 3 km long and varying from 100 m to 280 m in height. Numerous other tumuli measure less than 50 m across. Virtually all of the larger tumuli

FIGURE 28.1 Some of the lavas that form the present floor of Tycho. Two volcanic tumuli, with elongated source vents controlled by fractures, are marked **T**. Smaller, similar features can be seen near to **v**. The scale is in km. [Lunar Orbiter V, NASA]

DOI: 10.1201/9781003181279-28   125

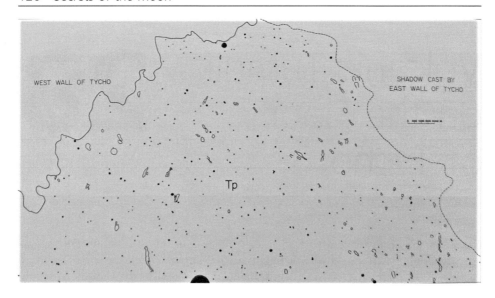

FIGURE 28.2   Map of vents on the N floor of Tycho. The elongated vents tend to trend in the principal directions of the grid system. [R. Strom[40]]

seem to have cracked open, or they feature elongate craters that are spread along the crest of each tumulus. The tumuli themselves follow the directions of the principal grid lineaments. Again, by reference to Strom's map[40] (Fig. 28.2) of other probable volcanic vents set in the northern parts of Tycho's floor it is seen that, not only do the vents tend to be linear, but they are also aligned with the grid system families A, B and C. All these properties are strongly indicative of the extrusive origin of the lavas.

FIGURE 28.3   Mare domes near to Marius (41 km diameter) in Oceanus Procellarum. [Lunar Orbiter II, NASA]

FIGURE 28.4   A small lava dome of basaltic pahoehoe lava, Mauna Loa, Hawaii. [G. Fielder]

I estimate that the mean slopes of the larger tumuli range from 10° to 22°. Clearly, these tumuli are unlike the large domes (Fig. 28.3) seen in the lunar maria. Many mare domes slope at a mere 2° or 3°, which is consistent with the relative fluidity of the mare lavas; although some mare domes (probably even later differentiates) display somewhat steeper slopes than those. Like terrestrial shield volcanoes, the domes in maria are frequently topped by a caldera. Well-known examples of these domes are found in the diameter range 10 km to several tens of kilometers. Other lunar domes might be much smaller: a Hawaiian lava dome of extruded basaltic lava as small as a few metres across is shown in Fig. 28.4. Both types of excrescence, tumular and domical, are volcanic: their different sizes, slopes and other characteristics attest to lavas that differ in viscosity, probably because of a process involving progresssive differentiation.

The Unusual Rocks of Tycho, Copernicus and Aristarchus

29

We have known since the nineteen-sixties that certain physical properties of the rocks of Tycho, Copernicus and Aristarchus differ markedly from the same properties of most other parts of the lunar surface. During an eclipse of the Moon, Tycho, Copernicus and Aristarchus, all radiate more heat than their surroundings (R. Shorthill et al.[41]). Heated during the times they are exposed to sunlight, these large craters continue to radiate heat – and more than average – when the sunlight is obscured by the Earth's shadow. The accepted inference is that the rocks characteristic of these craters have the capacity to conduct and retain more solar heat than have the rocks elsewhere on the Moon. Tycho also exhibits anomalously strong radar reflectivity, which the authors G. Pettengill and J. Henry[42] attributed to very much rougher, or very much denser, rocks than others on the Moon. More recent work showing that Tycho, in particular, has a floor of exceptionally high thermal inertia has been published by Hayne[76] et al.

It is satisfying to find a reason for these anomalies in the late, viscous flows that coat the terrain outside the walls of Tycho, in the other flows squeezing down between obstacles in its inner terraces and, most importantly, in the large volumes of pristine-looking lava that cover the original floor of Tycho. In Tycho, we see little evidence for regolith cover; possibly, the recency and the advanced differentiation of the Tycho lavas expose their relatively unworked, radar-reflective surfaces in comparison with the surfaces of other lavas such as those in the maria where, we have seen, they are capped with underdense regolith.

DOI: 10.1201/9781003181279-29

Cracks in Tycho and Kilauea

30

The very revealing Lunar Orbiter 5 photomosaic reproduced in Fig. 27.3 clearly depicts ropy lavas in the northern part of the floor of Tycho as well as lavas, displaying arcuate flow-ridging, that were extruded from sources in the terraced, northern walls of the crater. Significantly, the picture also shows that the floor is cracked in a zone, measuring several hundred metres wide, around its periphery, bringing to mind the cracks that are commonly found in the lava-filled calderas of the Earth.

Active basaltic volcanism is fundamental to the formation of the Hawaiian chain of islands. Calderas such as Kilauea (Fig. 30.1), underlain by magmas, are formed by collapse. Periodically, liquid magmas surge up and erupt to deliver a lake of lava in a part of, or the whole of, the caldera. If, after cooling, a crust forms on the lake and the

FIGURE 30.1 The lava floor of Kilauea, Hawaii, showing peripheral cracking. Polygonal cracking in the central, active parts of the floor is a characteristic effect of many small cells of convection. [G. Fielder]

DOI: 10.1201/9781003181279-30

fluids beneath it drain back through underlying conduits, the lava can subside, causing the crust to warp downwards, especially towards the middle of the caldera. This bending induces stresses in the crust. In response, fractures tend to form in the coolest and most stretched, pivotal parts of the lava crust, around the inner edges of a caldera (Fig. 30.1).

Tycho's peripheral fractures, from less than 10 m or 20 m wide, appear to have formed in similar fashion after the floor lavas around the edges had developed a solid crust. Interestingly, the fractures curve continuously across the toe of the lava flow marked **f** in Fig. 27.3; so this lava lobe had also congealed and hardened before the fracturing process.

Central Peaks and the Impact Process

31

Fractures (Fig. 31.1) are also present along the base of Tycho's larger, and higher, group of central mountains, which reach a height of some 2 km above the floor. Adding to these observations in 2009, NASA's Lunar Reconnaissance Orbiter produced stunning, oblique images of Tycho's central eminences and associated floor fractures (Fig. 31.2). The fractures near to these central mountains are linear, rather than curved, and, like the mountains themselves, tend to adhere to the principal directions of the grid system. Lesser lineaments that sympathise with one or more of these directions clearly traverse some of the central mountains photographed by Lunar Reconnaissance Orbiter.

The positive relationship between the gross trends of each of many lunar central blocks and the grid system was discussed by R. Chapman and me.[43] We also questioned R. Baldwin's contention that the offsets of lunar central peaks from the centres of their respective craters resulted from the oblique impacts of meteoroids, since the directions of offset tended to relate to the principal grid lineament directions. While Baldwin[44] considered that craters like Tycho and Copernicus showed little or no evidence for isostatic recovery, he proposed that the central mountains of craters had been subjected to a rebound mechanism: "whenever an impact occurs…. there is a rebound in the center". The evidence for that comes from observations of explosion cratering on the Earth. Indeed, most people will have observed the rebound that occurs when a drop of water falls into a bowl of water: high-speed impacts will also behave hydrodynamically, initially. Yet I think that the new, high-resolution pictorial evidence provided by the Lunar Reconnaissance Orbiter adds weight to the theory of early magmatic intrusion and, in some instances, later volcanic extrusion processes that I now envisage for the formation of lunar central mountains.

Using a Lunar Orbiter 5 photograph of Tycho's highest central block, Strom[40] found a lava lake occupying a rectilinear depression that measured 1 km × 0.5 km. Now, a Lunar Reconnaissance Orbiter photograph (Fig. 31.3) shows much more clearly that this lava lake carries linear fractures and ridges that are parallel to the direction of lineaments seen in both the LO V and LRO images. Somehow, it appears that magmas – probably from deep in the lunar crust – rose up one or more of the principal fissures of the grid system and, occasionally, the magmas wedged through finer fractures to reach the summits of some central eminences. Possibly, outgassing would "blow off the lid" and create a fracture-controlled depression or crater into which lavas could exude.

DOI: 10.1201/9781003181279-31

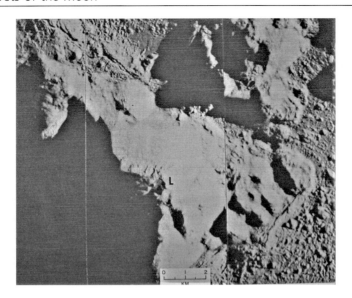

FIGURE 31.1   Tycho's principal central mountain showing the fracturing along the base and the lava lake **L**, identified by Strom, at or near to the summit. [Lunar Orbiter V, NASA]

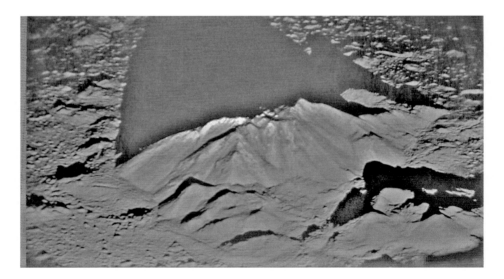

FIGURE 31.2   This Lunar Reconnaissance Orbiter (LRO) photograph shows the central group of mountains of Tycho, which measure about 15 km from bottom left to top right. Fractures in the floor of Tycho, which seem to follow the directions of the grid system, can be seen flanking the bases of the mountains. North is to the right. The lava lake of Strom, identified in Fig. 31.1, nestles in the depression seen in the summit of the highest mountain, about 2 km above the floor. For detail, see Fig. 31.3. [LRO, NASA/GSFC/Arizona State University]

FIGURE 31.3   Here is a most remarkable LRO photograph of the lake mentioned in the previous two figures. North is, again, to the right. Grid lineaments, as dyke-like outcrops, slice through the mountains, while the lake discussed in figures 31.1 and 31.2 is now found to be incised by parallel fractures which follow the direction of the principal, dyke-like outcrops. Clearly, there have been tectonic movements since the lava infilled the depression. The light-toned, semi-rounded block of rock, which measures about 120 m across, has cracks and other lineations in it and a study of these features in relation to the prevailing lineaments in its vicinity will help to decide its origin. [LRO, NASA/GSFC/Arizona State University]

Other authors have suggested that the lava lake that is set in the highest central mountain of Tycho was produced when impact melt fell back immediately after the excavation of the 100 km diameter crater. The collective evidence from the dating of the many lava lakes of Tycho would of course argue against this interpretation, for the lava lakes formed at a much later time than the event that formed the bulk of Tycho. On the other hand, in the case of craters having diameters of only 20 km and less, Neish et al.[81] have shown that flows external to the walls of these craters frequently occur immediately outside the lowest point of their rims and the authors argue that these flows, characteristically rough in the centimetre to decimetre range as revealed by the 12.6 cm radar of the LRO mission, are indeed of impact melt. It would be of interest to have a comparison of the dates of these deposits and their associated craters.

It is important to ask why the axis of each central mountain of Tycho tends to be aligned with a grid direction. I can think of two ways that this can be explained. One is that the mountains themselves are primarily post-impact extrusive phenomena. The other is that the mountains represent exposed, indurated and fracture-controlled structures that were essentially below the surface before the impact event that excavated Tycho. Following J. H. Mädler, it is generally reported that the majority of central mountain blocks of lunar craters do not attain the mean level of the terrain that surrounds those craters. However, it is difficult to assess the mean level of the terrain beyond the ringwalls of many of the highland craters because these craters were

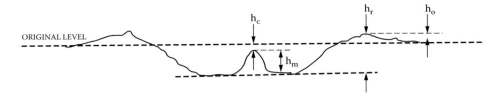

FIGURE 31.4   Profile of a lunar crater with central peak. Not to scale. $h_c = h_r - (h_o + h_m)$. For Tycho, $h_c = 4.8 - (h_o + 2)$ km. With $h_o = 1$ km, $h_c = 1.8$ km below outside level. For $h_o = 3$ km, $h_c = 0.2$ km *above* outside level. [G. Fielder]

formed on pre-cratered terrain that was, at the very least, undulatory. Making an estimate of the mean external slope of the walls of Tycho, for example, is anything but straightforward. Among the group of central mountains of Tycho, the highest mountain, rises (please refer to Fig. 31.4 and its caption) to about $h_m = 2$ km above the mean floor level. The heights of the ringwall mountains of Tycho differ around the circumference of the crater: to the east and west of the centre of Tycho the highest parts of the ringwall reach about $h_r = 4.8$ km above the mean floor. But any estimate of the mean height, h_o, of the ringwall above the *original* (or even the present) mean level of the terrain that is external to the crater is bound to be unreliable.

When discussing possible rebound and isostatic adjustments of parts of craters, it would be helpful to have meaningful values of h_o. The way forward might be to measure the appropriate parameters of craters sited in areas where surrounding craters are sparse; but the majority of large craters were formed in areas of saturation cratering; and, for them, resort might have to be made to a comparison method. For example, in the case of Tycho, the like-sized crater Copernicus might be examined. Exterior blanketing seems to extend for at least one diameter measured from the centre of Copernicus and estimates of h_o, obtained from published contour maps, range very roughly from 1 km to 3 km. Referring again to the formula given in Fig. 31.4, and applying these numbers to Tycho indicates that h_c might range from 1.8 km below the surrounding level to 0.2 km above that level. Perhaps Mädler's rule should be treated with suspicion in application to the majority of highland craters.

A concise account of the cratering mechanics appropriate to high-speed impacts has been given by King.[45] A more detailed, theoretical treatment tied to some observations was presented by Gold.[84] No one has witnessed a cratering event of the size of Tycho, so that should be borne in mind when following my attempt to describe the salient points in the formation of Tycho. Had Tycho, nominal diameter 100 km, been formed by a mid-velocity – say, 10 km/sec – impact, the impactor might have been a meteoroid about 10 km in diameter. The first contact with the Moon would have generated intense pressures through shock waves in both the lunar crust and the incoming object. The meteoroid would have deformed and, probably, most of it would have vaporised. The lunar materials themselves would, first, have behaved hydrodynamically and would have been expelled as molten fragments at all azimuths centred on the impact site by a process known as jetting. Evidence for that might be expected to be found in omnidirectional lunar rays; but the jetted fragments would be moving so fast that they would leave the Moon. The continuing downwards and lateral propagation of the main shock front would compress and shift the lunar materials away from the central areas to scour out most of the crater, eject the ray-forming bodies and create the crater walls as the velocities of ejection reduced quickly. Materials would be ejected in a base surge over the rim of the crater, mostly at small angles to the horizontal. Either the inherent structure of the deep, central blocks escaped eradication or the blocks were modified, after the impact, by an extrusive, and possible uplift, process.

The Crater Aristarchus

32

Aristarchus (40 km in diameter), is shown in Fig. 32.1. Its southern floor, enlarged in Fig. 32.2, again shows clear evidence of curvilinear peripheral fracturing and, therefore, of subsidence. Here, in what is a crater less than half the size of Tycho, the width of the fracture zone that lies along the periphery of the floor of Aristarchus is only 2 km or so. The fractures themselves are up to 30 m wide at the surface. The central mountain, shown on a beautiful photograph (Fig. 32.3) taken from the LRO in 2011, rises to 3.5 km or more above the floor and is surfaced by materials that differ in their mutual reflectivity. What appears to be the outcrop of a darker dyke is visible; but, overall, the mountain remains one of the brighest spots on the Moon.

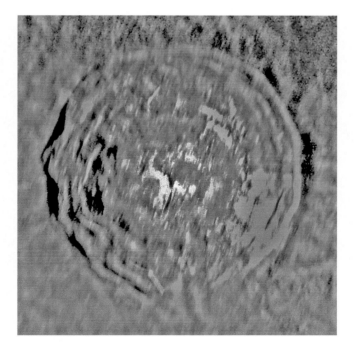

FIGURE 32.1   The crater Aristarchus. [Lunar Orbiter V, NASA]

DOI: 10.1201/9781003181279-32

FIGURE 32.2   The southern floor of Aristarchus, showing fractures to either side of **D**, in the zone of maximum radial tensions as a result of downwarping of the crater's floor. [Lunar Orbiter V, NASA]

FIGURE 32.3   The central mountain of Aristarchus. [LRO, NASA/GSFC/Arizona State University]

Images taken in the visible and UV parts of the spectrum by the Hubble Advance Camera for Surveys pointed to the presence of ilmenite; while NASA's Lunar Prospector (1978) found radon-222 emissions that could be indicative of ongoing volcanic activity. As in the case of Tycho, the variously sized tumuli in Aristarchus have pronounced, axial trends that follow the directions of the lineament families A, B and C of the grid system.

The same trends are seen in other, linear floor features in Aristarchus. Many fractures are strung with small craters. Some of these craters might have been formed by collapse into vacuous fissures following the withdrawal of magmas. Others might have been formed by explosive outgassing.

The Crater Copernicus

33

Copernicus (Fig. 26.1) is another striking ray-crater, nearly as big as Tycho. Although the rays of Copernicus are not as long as those of Tycho, their visibility is enhanced by their trespassing across the dark floors of Mare Imbrium, Sinus Aestuum and the northern parts of Oceanus Procellarum where they join the rays of Aristarchus and Kepler (31 km in diameter). The ray-elements (Fig. 26.3) of Copernicus trace back to its annular floor, which surrounds the central mountains (Fig. 33.1). Several lava flows may again be recognised, some having run inwards down the north wall terraces. Again, there are lava lakes in and around the walls of Copernicus. The lavas would rise under the hydrostatic pressure caused by the burden of the ringwalls.

The lava floor of Copernicus (Fig. 33.2) has, again, its hills, some with cratered summits, and its tumuli, a few seen to be associated with fracturing. The central blocks of mountains (Fig. 33.1) – more dispersed than those of Tycho – which have slopes of 30° or so (but progressively less than that towards the contact with the floor as a result of downslope movement or "mass wasting" of materials) rise up to some

FIGURE 33.1 An oblique view of the interior of Copernicus. [Lunar Orbiter II, NASA]

DOI: 10.1201/9781003181279-33

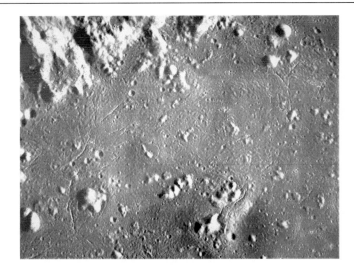

FIGURE 33.2   The lava floor of Copernicus with its volcanic landforms. [Lunar Orbiter V, NASA]

1.3 km above the floor and are again dissected, and controlled, by the underlying grid fractures.

While the evidence for extrusion of floor materials is again strong, the fractures in the lava floor of Copernicus tend to follow the grid directions in floor regions near to both the walls and the central peaks; so the evidence for floor subsidence is not as strong as in the case of Tycho.

Dating the Lavas of Tycho and Aristarchus

34

In order to date each lava unit in these craters, I needed to count the numbers of primary impact craters on it. Then, given the relevant impact rate, the numbers of these small craters per unit area of each lava flow and lava lake, as well as the numbers in the lava floor, could be used for dating purposes. Unlike the terraced walls of the large craters, the lava units are relatively smooth and unshadowed and, therefore, super-imposed craters down to a certain size can be recognised and counted with little or no concern about observational losses. Strom and I started by isolating eumorphic, circular craters, with diameters greater than 50 m, in each of the Lunar Orbiter areas of interest that centred on Tycho. We used a planimeter to measure the respective areas that were covered by the counts.

Consistently, we found that higher number-densities of our selected craters occurred in stratigraphically older units. This indicated that most of the counts related to primary impact craters, rather than to endogenic or secondary craters. (In the case of craters smaller than 50 m, and more than 20 m, across we found an excess of craters on the generally later, most viscous-looking flows of Tycho; and we think that these craters might be endogenic.) Returning to the craters >50 m in diameter, we found that the mean crater density on all the large lakes, of summed area 22 km^2, outside the eastern walls of Tycho, was essentially the same as on the floor unit, area 460 km^2. These counts indicated that the lakes and floor unit were both extruded at times of around 1.5×10^8 years ago. The more viscous rim flows appeared to be about twice as old (3.2×10^8 years).

In Aristarchus, crater counting, as well as the consideration of the distribution of fractures in the floor (Fig. 32.2) points to crater populations that differ between different floor areas. This evidence would be consistent with a covering, such as ash deposits or late flows, that was restricted to the central parts of the floor. We concentrated on the oldest, more fractured portions of the floor of Aristarchus and found that these parts were emplaced 2.3×10^8 years ago – later than most of the rim flows which averaged 4.3×10^8 years in age. These flows are thinner, longer and smoother than the flows associated with Tycho's floor. This is, perhaps, not surprising since Aristarchus is situated in a mare-type region, where low-viscosity flows can be found, rather than an upland region, where shorter, more viscous flows can be found.

DOI: 10.1201/9781003181279-34

In the cases of both Tycho and Aristarchus, times of up to 2×10^8 years had elapsed, it seemed, between the earlier, and the later, volcanic episodes. That seems to be a significant observation and I shall return to it shortly.

The viscous flows in the outer walls of Tycho are stratigraphically higher than a flow unit (Fig. 34.1) which we think might be a base surge deposit laid down when the giant impact that produced Tycho occurred. Dating this deposit, using crater counts, showed that it was produced some 7×10^8 years ago. In the case of Aristarchus, we dated another possible base surge flow to 1.1×10^9 years ago. These could be the respective dates of the impact events that triggered the production of Tycho and Aristarchus.

In mapping and grouping large craters in relative age brackets, the United States Geological Survey at Flagstaff, then under the direction of G. Shoemaker, placed Tycho, Copernicus, Aristarchus and Kepler in one and the same "Copernican" period. Later, spot measurements of actual ages of rocks in parts of the Moon enabled the

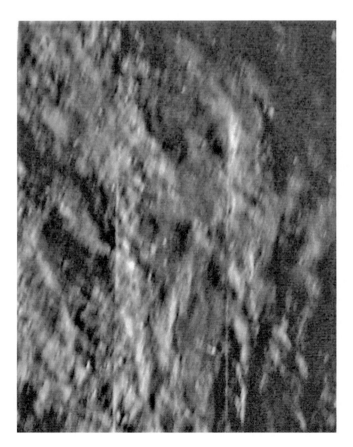

FIGURE 34.1   Part of the possible base surge deposit that might have accompanied the production of Tycho some 7×10^8 years ago. [Lunar Orbiter V, NASA]

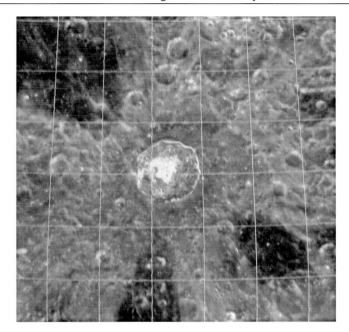

FIGURE 34.2 The "Copernican period" crater Jackson (71 km diameter). Like Tycho, Jackson is associated with a prominent dark halo. [LAC 51, The Clementine Atlas of the Moon, D.B.J. Bussey and P.D. Spudis. © D.B.J. Bussey and P.D. Spudis 2004. Reproduced with permission of the Licensor through PLSclear]

USGS to estimate the spread in the real ages of each period which they assigned to lunar rocks. The Copernican period is now thought to stretch over the last 10^9 years, in pleasing agreement with our results for Tycho and Aristarchus.

Other craters, such as Jackson (Fig. 34.2), Proclus (28 km diameter, 16°N, 47°E) and Giodano Bruno (22 km diameter, 36°N, 103°E) were also placed in the Copernican period. Possibly these craters are of mixed origin, too. Detailed studies, similar to those that I have described for Tycho and Aristarchus, will help to reveal their stories.

The Origin of the Lavas in Impact Craters

35

Before I attempt to describe the history of a formation such as Tycho, I need to find what caused the remarkable outpourings of lava that Strom and I described. We have reasoned that titanic amounts of energy were required to excavate ring structures of 100 km size and that this came in the form of kinetic energy of meteoroids. Of the associated volcanic features that we are now able to see, a few had been noted by assiduous lunar observers over the decades; but only now can the past dichotomy of opinions on the origins of craters like Tycho be understood.

Part of the kinetic energy of impact would, of course, go into shocking the projectile and some of the country rocks. The question is, would the energy transferred into heat be sufficient to provide all the lavas that we see in and around the crater under consideration? Evidently not: not only are the observed volumes of lava very large but, as we have now seen, the volcanic eruptions occurred later, over time spans measured in hundreds of millions of years. By contrast, an impact process, even on the scale of Tycho, will terminate after a very short time.

We are left with the possibilities that large craters, at least, would eventually generate deep melting as a result of natural, post-impact adjustments; or that the impacts would open pre-existing crustal fractures, in the process accessing magmas deeper in the Moon. Given the right temperatures in the lunar crust an isostatic process, which would involve the load of a freshly formed ringwall tending to move downwards and the newly excavated basin of a crater tending to move upwards, might be expected. My Research Associate G. Hulme demonstrated[46] that, during the recovery of a large crater, viscous dissipative heating in the lunar lithosphere might well have contributed to the melting of the rocks beneath the crater at depths of about one quarter of its diameter. Hulme estimated that any initial melting and extrusion might take little more than 10^4 years for the largest craters, rising to 10^7 years for the smaller craters (with diameters in the region of a few tens of kilometers). These time scales appear to be too short to account for the late flows that Strom and I described in and around Tycho; but lavas from the viscous dissipative heating mechanism might occur elsewhere. The weight per unit basal area of the walls would reduce as a result of slumping and terrace formation in the immediately post-impact period. More particularly, the evidence we now see in the peripheral floor fractures is for the downwarping, rather than the upwarping, of the lava floors. Of course, excavated materials have been replaced, to some unknown extent, by lavas that are possibly the denser. And, whether the lavas derived from great depths under general hydrostatic pressure or from smaller depths under the influence of isostatic adjustments, the evidence for deep fracturing and the much later rise and extrusion of lavas from grid fractures beneath a crater is plentiful. For Tycho, following Hulme, I conclude that most of the lavas probably originated at a depth in excess of 25 km. These deep melts would rise hydrostatically.

The relationship between the principle trends of the grid system and the linear fractures in the tumuli, walls, floors and central mountains of the large craters studied proves not only that the fractures are deep seated but also that they are of more consequence for the rise of magmas than are the random access routes in any residual, brecciated rocks that must have been created beneath the craters by the impacts. As the impact craters that we have examined came late in the period of large crater formation, it is most probable that they simply added to the pre-brecciation of the crustal rocks. Seismometers, placed on the lunar surface by the Apollo astronauts of six successive missions recorded signals that, uncharacteristic of seismic signals on Earth, built up gradually but faded extremely slowly. These records were of impacts of small meteoroids (the events measuring only from 1 to 3 on the Richter scale) and of planned impacts of a Lunar Module (after use by the Apollo 12 team) and of the Saturn 4B booster rocket (used in the Apollo 13 mission). While the smaller events gave signals which may have taken an hour or so to fade, the signals of the bigger, artificial impacts persisted for several hours. This led to the theory that the rocks forming the upper parts of the Moon were extensively fractured. (More details can be found in N. Short.[47]) Therefore, it is arguable that large volumes of intensely broken, readily shifted rocks were removed from a late impact site during the excavation phase, leaving largely systematically-fractured rocks under a crater floor. In this way, rising magmas (Fig. 35.1) would, in general, be able to utilize major ascent channels rather than act to weld together minor pieces of jumbled rock and detritus.

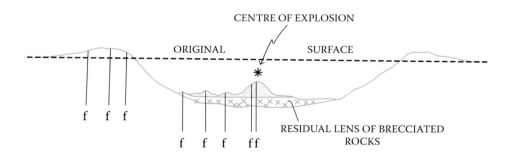

FIGURE 35.1   Sketch (not to scale) of proposed, vertical section of a large crater, formed by high speed impact, in which process a meteoroid penetrates by a few of its diameters before exploding to excavate the crater and leave, initially, a thin lens of breccia. Later, magma rises up fractures, or fissures, labelled f, under hydrostatic pressure and lavas are extruded from fractures in the walls, central mountains and floor as they adjust isostatically (under gravity). [G. Fielder]

Support for some of these deductions came, in 2012, from a remarkable NASA mission called GRAIL – Gravity Recovery and Interior Laboratory – in which twin spacecraft, named Ebb and Flow, were delivered to polar orbits around the Moon, first at a height of 55 km, later at only 23 km above the surface. The object was to resolve small differences in lunar gravity that were caused by sub-surface structures such as igneous intrusions and, hence, to evaluate their locations, sizes and distributions. To emphasize features like dykes, beneath the surface, the gravitational effects of the lunar topography were removed by the use of laser altimetry data from the Lunar Reconnaissance Orbiter. To this end, Ebb and Flow were separated in their orbits by a nominal 200 km. The different gravitational attractions that a crustal anomaly had on the two satellites resulted in the separation between them changing slightly and this differential separation was measured to within a few 100ths of a micron!

The results (J. Andrews-Hanna et al.[48]) were striking and allowed the recognition of all intrusions that were substantial enough to produce high-density contrasts with the surrounding rocks. In other words, the method was able to see the largest and most significant intrusions, and these were mapped by the authors. In particular, many linear gravity anomalies, which the authors classified as probable or possible examples, were found to be distributed uniformly in families across the whole of the Moon (Fig. 35.2). Notably, taking all the linear gravity anomalies together, they seem to follow the trends of systems A and B of the grid system quite closely.

The authors interpreted the best-defined anomalies as relating to broad (widths 5 km to 25 km) dykes that cut, as vertical sheets, through the crustal rocks for several

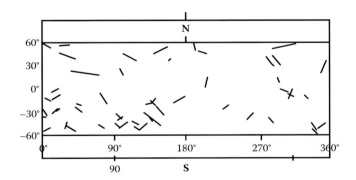

FIGURE 35.2 This diagram shows the approximate positions and directions of the linear gravity anomalies mapped by Andrews-Hanna et al.[48] They designated some as "probable" and others as "possible" anomalies: I have treated these two classes as of equal weight and have combined them in this figure. Andrews-Hanna et al presented their results in cylindrical projection so I have reproduced only those parts of their map that lie within the latitudes ±60°. Even so, the angles between the lines representing intersecting linear anomalies are correct only for regions that are close to the lunar equator. This representation shows the results for the near side of the Moon at the left (0° to 90° longitude) and right (270° to 360°) sides of this diagram, whilst the results for the far side of the Moon are to be found in the 90° to 270° range of longitude. [Modified from J.C. Andrews-Hanna et al., Science, **339,** 2013, p. 676, Fig. 1C]

tens of kilometres – possibly through to the interface of the crust and mantle of the Moon. It is here that we might look for the source regions of the magmas. My observations of fine surface lineaments as well as of the volcanism in and around the large craters that I have studied would seem to require a multitude of narrower dykes near to the surface and, indeed, the GRAIL data would permit (but not necessarily resolve) such dyke-swarms.

Tensions in the Lunar Crust

36

In order to explain how magmas from depth were able to rise through sub-vertical fissures (long fractures that have opened) Andrews-Hanna et al. deduced that the lunar crust must have suffered an expansive phase. Furthermore, because the dykes that cross under old craters (and even under Mare Crisium) lack surface expressions, the authors argue that the dykes in question are even older than these features; so the tensile phase in the crust is likely to date from very early (4.2 to 4.5×10^9 years ago) in lunar history.

My first argument for a tensile phase in lunar history arose through my interest in rilles. All lunar rilles are negative topographic features that, broadly, take the form of trenches. (The name rille derives from the German for trench.) Normal rilles are straight in trend and have fairly linear edges from which the walls slope inwards. They can, however, occur en-echelon, a property that is likely to indicate underlying shearing (strike-slip faulting), and can cut through ridges that have slumped where they cross over the rille. They can be up to 5 km wide and up to about 800 ± 200 m deep. A good example is to be found in the Ariadaeus rille (Fig. 9.2). Normal rilles like the Ariadaeus rille can display flat or humped floors. Other examples of humped floors are shown in two parts of the Sirsalis rille (Figs. 36.1 and 36.2) and, possibly, in one or two of the rilles located at and around 2°.5 N, 77° W, within Hedin.

Crater rilles exhibit crateriform walls, as in the case of the Hyginus Rille (Figs. 36.3; and cf. Figs. 9.2 and 12.5) and, again, the walls slope only inwards; hence, the craters themselves might have been produced purely by collapse. In cases where the craters are contiguous, the walls of contact are low or missing. However, drainage of regolith would not necessarily have led to a row of crater-shaped depressions in which the arc of a crater wall on one side of a rille was symmetrically opposed by a matching wall-arc on the other side; and that circumstance might suggest that the forms of these craters were produced by the sudden expansion of pockets of gas in lavas that rose up fractures and undermined the local regolith while transferring little material to the country immediately surrounding the rille. (See also Fielder [21].)

Arcuate rilles (Fig. 36.4) have some of the characteristics of normal rilles but are restricted to the peripherae of maria and some craters. In the case of a mare location, arcuate rilles – some with raised central ridges – have the trench-like characteristics of normal rilles, indicating the subsidence of near-surface materials into underlying, tensile fractures: these fractures are a product of local stressing combined with more general, global stressing. Arcuate rilles do occur in some craters other than maria; and these rilles

DOI: 10.1201/9781003181279-36

FIGURE 36.1 The north end of the Sirsalis Rille showing some central ridges within it. [LRO, NASA]

FIGURE 36.2   Mid, and south end of, Sirsalis Rille showing its cutting through de Vico A. [Lunar Orbiter IV, NASA]

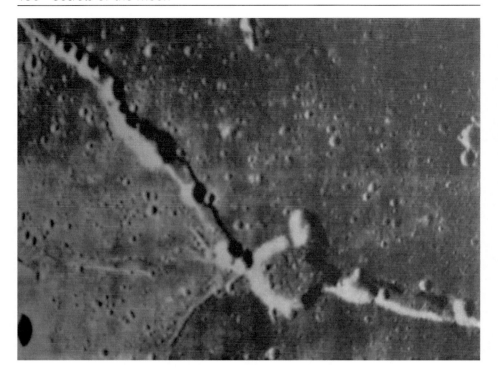

FIGURE 36.3   An enlarged (morning) view of the Hyginus crater-rille. [LO V, NASA]. The crater-rille may be viewed again under morning illumination (Fig. 12.5) and in the afternoon (Fig. 9.2) views.

are to be distinguished from the peripheral cracking or fissuring that can be seen in lava floors with little or no regolith cover, as in the case of Tycho (see Section 30).

When I first studied[49] the 270 km long, 4 km wide Ariadaeus Rille (Figs. 9.2 and 12.5) I found it to be a subsidence feature, probably underlain by a dyke. I thought that the dyke might have followed what geologists term a second-order strike-slip fault. I was aware that terrestrial magmas rarely ascend along strike-slip faults because they are formed under crustal pressures that tend to prevent them from opening. So, I reasoned that the lunar crust had been subjected to a tensile phase that came later than the original faulting.

Then, in 1962, when I was working with B. Warner on a problem concerning the peculiar ridge and trough patterns[50] around certain large craters, I stumbled on an independent way of assessing the general lunar crustal stress regime at the time when the craters were formed.

The first thing that one might notice about the linear features that are seen to splay out around each crater is that some of them are approximately radial to the crater: they may be reminiscent of short rays. The second thing to notice is that, unlike rays, the lineaments are composed of ridges, troughs, and some chains of small craters; and that, importantly, these features are definitely not all radial to their associated crater. Each crater has four bundles of sub-radial lineaments, and only the central lineament of each

FIGURE 36.4   Arcuate rilles at the eastern edge of Mare Humorum. [LO IV, NASA]

bundle traces back through the centre of a crater. Observing visually from the Pic-du-Midi Observatory, I first noted[51] that the lineaments around Aristillus (Fig. 36.5) and Aristoteles did not sweep around the respective craters continuously. Rather, they exhibited "gaps" where radial lineaments were few or missing, after the manner shown in Fig 36.6. The central lineament of a bundle runs in the direction of either system A or system B of the grid system. So the system A bundles are found on the SE and NW sides of a crater and the system B bundles are, roughly, orthogonal to them. The practised eye will note these properties in the particularly well developed patterns around Timocharis (33 km diameter) and Euler (27 km), the pattern around Euler being depicted in Fig. 36.7. Near to each crater, the sub-radial lineaments wheel away from the straight-jacket imposed by the pre-existing stresses of the grid system. I think that this happened because of additional stresses imposed on the lunar crust by the creation of a large crater. Far from being deposits of ejecta, the sub-radial lineaments must have a fault-related origin.

In an isotropic, unstressed elastic medium any stresses generated around a forming explosion crater would lead, essentially, to radial and circumferential fracturing. In fact, the observations of sub-radial lineaments require the Moon's near-surface layers to have been in a state of stress before the large craters in question were formed. My theory[50] involves superimposing the stresses caused by cratering on the stress field already in the crust. The analysis showed that the crustal layers down to at least the

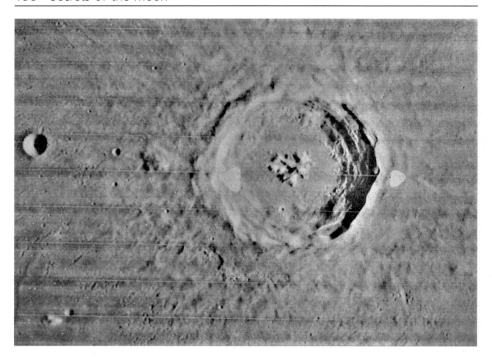

FIGURE 36.5   Aristillus and its sub-radial pattern. [LO IV, NASA]

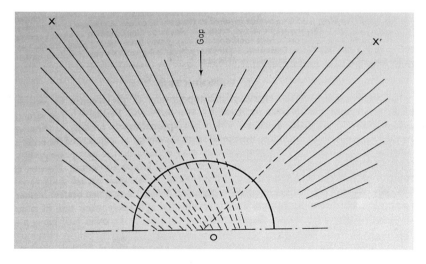

FIGURE 36.6   Diagram showing the "gaps" between bundles of sub-radial lineaments around a crater. [G. Fielder]

FIGURE 36.7   Euler, 27 km in diameter, and its sub-radial pattern of lineaments, shown in three frames of Apollo 17 that have been mosaicked. The lineaments may be grouped into four bundles in which only the central axis of each bundle is radial to the crater and follows the direction of either System A (NW to SE) or System B (NE to SW). Other lineaments of each bundle are distinctly non-radial to Euler. Remarkably, many photogeologists are still referring to such non-radial lineaments as "radial throwout", even though the original observations refuting similar claims were published[50] some 58 years ago. Note the many chains of craters, particularly to the S and W of Euler, that have trends which tend to intersect at about a right-angle. When extrapolated, most of the linear chains, like the other lineaments, do not pass through the centre of Euler. The chains of craters almost certainly originated in fractures and are very probably endocraters rather than secondary impact craters. [Apollo 17, NASA]

depths of a few kilometres, influenced by large impacts (and down to tens of kilo-metres when influenced by very large impacts) must have been stressed in tension at the time when many – probably most – of the craters were formed.

By analysing the lengths of the central lineaments of the bundles of lineaments associated with the eighteen craters that were listed in our original paper, Warner and I found that the tension in the surface rocks of the Moon, at the time when the craters were formed, varied little across the entire near side of the Moon. Because certain craters on the far side of the Moon are, like many on the near side, associated with their own sub-radial lineament systems, and because of the GRAIL observations across both the near and far sides of the Moon, I am sure that the entire surface of the Moon suffered tensile stressing for a long time. The time set by the analysis of the craters with sub-radial lineaments would be at least a billion years, which is the estimated age of the largest Copernican craters discussed here; yet some older craters, for example Aristoteles, also have sub-radial lineaments: they push back the times over which the tensions operated to the Eratosthenian age bracket of 1 to 3.15 billion years. As the GRAIL authors suggest, this general, tensile regime in the lunar crust was caused, possibly, by mantle expansion. I think that occurred as a result of the very early internal heating processes already discussed, together with the later heating from radioactivity, the continuing frictional heating from tidal forces, and the good insulating properties of the lunar crust. The early pressure tending to keep grid system joints closed must have been relieved to allow the ascending magmas to fill fissures and fractures and, with the right hydrostatic conditions, to reach the lunar surface.

Is There Any Current Volcanic Activity on the Moon?

37

Looking at other large Copernican craters sited around the Moon, I find that past volcanism, in and around them, is not uncommon. As regards present volcanic activity, it is more difficult to be certain. Telescopic observers of the Moon have regularly reported transient events in specific parts of the surface. Transient events on the Moon include sightings of brightenings, glows and obscurations, some of them reddish, and there are many such reports in the literature and on-line. For example, in 1787 W. Herschel saw what he assumed were three active volcanoes in the dark portion of the Moon. In any visual report, it is important to obtain confirmation from a reliable source. In 1963, such a visual observation of reddish glows in the vicinity of Aristarchus was reported by Greenacre and Barr (see reference 21). Better still, observers should try to make a permanent record of any transient event.

On 3 November, 1958, N. Kosyrev and V. Ezersky were using the 50-inch reflector of the Crimean Astrophysical Observatory when they noticed a reddish cloud followed by a whitish brightening on the eastern flank of the central mountain of the crater Alphonsus (Fig. 37.1). The anomalous brightness fell to its normal value after half an hour. Taken together, these effects lasted for 1 ½ hours, giving time for Kosyrev to obtain spectrograms (photographs of spectra) of the area. Kosyrev visited the University of London Observatory in May, 1966 and, later, I drove him around parts of the West End. He earnestly discussed the spectra of the phenomena in Alphonsus that he had obtained and evaluated to deduce that he and Ezersky observed emissions of gas as well as what he, Kosyrev, believed to be freshly erupted lava. If correct, Kosyrev had certainly made an exciting discovery, so I asked him if I could have a copy of the spectrum. After his return to the Crimea, he very kindly sent me a spectrogram, but it was not of a quality that would allow the confirmation of his deductions. However, a careful analysis of his spectra was completed by A. Kalinyak and L. Kamionko[52]: they microphotometered the spectra and concluded that the emissions in two parts of the spectrum were significant but were produced by a gas that fluoresced in the presence of solar radiation.

DOI: 10.1201/9781003181279-37

FIGURE 37.1   The "central" mountain and floor of Alphonsus. [Ranger IX, NASA]

Kosyrev again found a red anomaly on part of the central block of Alphonsus on 23 October, 1959. I conclude that there is a good chance that some observers have seen signs of activity, such as particulates rising in temporary clouds as a result of either gas escape or impacts. But definitive evidence for presently active volcanism on the Moon does seem to be lacking.

To summarise the history of large craters of the Tycho type, it is now clear that their origin has been complex, having involved dualism: impacts followed, very many years later, by volcanic differentiates that erupted into and around the craters through pre-extant grid system fractures and fissures in the lunar crust. These basaltic lavas were delivered through dykes reaching to the surface and originated at depths where magmatic differentiation and crystal fractionation could occur, rather than in areas very close to the surface.

Maria, Rilles and Wrinkle Ridges **38**

The dark areas of the lunar surface are a major feature of the near-side of the Moon. Such areas are of mutually low (about 5%) reflectivity and, collectively, their materials may be referred to as "lunabase". Several areas of lunabase tend to the circular or polygonal form and, of these, the largest are known as maria. Other lunabasic areas, notably Oceanus Procellarum, are irregular in outline. Long thought to be composed of basic lavas, samples returned from the Apollo missions indicated that the lunabase of the landing sites was indeed composed of volcanic lavas.

The circular and sub-circular areas of lunabase may best be explained if their formation was initiated by the impacts of large objects during the later phases of the accumulation of the Moon. There has been general support for the idea that Mare Imbrium, roughly 1200 km in diameter, and Mare Orientale (Figs. 38.1 and 38.2), roughly the same size, were originally deep basins produced by impact. The principal reason is that each is associated with very noticeable sub-radial lineament patterns that many lunar scientists have considered to be impact throwout. Although I found support for this idea when I first studied[53] Mare Imbrium, I now think that the theory in which materials are splashed out from the impact site to form, specifically, the sub-radial lineaments is wrong: less-ordered materials would have been splashed out first. Rather, the sub-radial lineaments of both Mare Imbrium and Mare Orientale were produced (see section 36) as a result of the net stresses that were active in the lunar crust during, and following, the respective impacts.

For Mare Imbrium, the location of the best-developed bundle of sub-radial lineaments (Fig. 5.2) is to be found in a large area around the central portion of the nearside face of the Moon; while there are few sub-radial lineaments in opposed directions (for example, to the north-west of Sinus Iridum, where the NE to SW lineaments (Fig. 5.4) of the Jura Mountains are in evidence.) The reason is, I think, that this is a region bordering on the north polar areas of the Moon where the lineament directions that are common in the Systems A and B of equatorial regions tend to be replaced by lineament directions that are randomised. This would explain why the sub-radial faulting of Mare Imbrium is not well developed to the north.

Lying closer to the equator than Mare Imbrium (its centre is at about latitude 30° N), Mare Orientale (centred at only 19° S) is probably the site of another highly energetic impact in which the hydrodynamical wave effects are well illustrated in the frozen, concentric rings (Fig. 38.3). In practice, the rings are not complete but tend to

FIGURE 38.1   One of the associated sub-radial bundles to the SE of Mare Orientale. [LO IV, NASA]

exhibit as arcs, successively larger arcs increasing in radius by a fixed amount of the square root of 2 multiplied by the radius of the adjacent smaller arc. This is Tresca's yield condition and flow rule for a centrally-loaded, plastic-rigid circular plate; and I showed[54] that there was good agreement between the predicted and measured radii of the rings that are centred in maria. At the time, I had used this concept to argue[21] that certain maria were downfaulted blocks of the lunar crust and that the theory could possibly be invoked to explain why some maria had polygonal margins. I had also reasoned that high-energy impacts would have led to symmetry - which is not observed - about an impact centre. However, I now think that the lack of symmetry about a central point could be related to the angle of impact of the body that initiated the crater and/or to pre-existing stressing or fracturing of the lunar crust.

It is established that mare basins have been at least partly filled with lavas. In this respect, note that the central surface of Mare Imbrium is, presently, several kilometres

FIGURE 38.2 Chart showing NW and SW bundles of lineaments related to Mare Orientale. [NASA/Lunar and Planetary Institute]

deeper than the edges. Any early upward adjustment could have been inhibited by the formation of deep concentrations of mass called "mascons" (to be discussed in Section 39) and by the accompanying extrusion of lavas. Successive lava flows (for example, Fig. 38.11) are seen to have carried the last lavas into Mare Imbrium - some from Oceanus Procellarum - and many of the observations of the distribution of small craters in maria can be explained if maria are surfaced with patchy lava flows, building on those that preceded them.

Arcuate rilles (Fig. 36.4) are found in the peripheral areas of some sub-circular maria. These rilles can be present in the lunabase or can cut through mountainous terrain. They

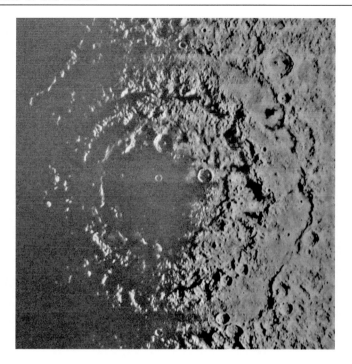

FIGURE 38.3   The outer and inner rings of mountains of Mare Orientale. [LO IV, NASA]

occur in the eastern and western borders of maria but fail to appear in the most northerly and southerly parts. This circumstance can be explained as a result of the combination of global east to west tensions that prevailed in the Moon before the arcuate rilles were formed and regional tectonic forces caused by downward adjustments of the mare materials. The fissures so produced acted as conduits for dykes which reached the surface only occasionally.

Wrinkle ridges frequently parallel arcuate rilles but the wrinkle ridges occur within the radii, centred in a mare, at which the rilles themselves appear. Wrinkle ridges even exhibit in the central regions of a mare (Fig. 38.4) and were controlled, principally, by the Moon-wide grid fractures. In the localities of the wrinkle ridges there was sufficient hydrostatic pressure to allow late dykes not only to convey lavas to the surface but to extrude and build significant ridges as well. This conclusion was first drawn from the research described in Section 3.

Although the central area of lunabase in Mare Orientale is smaller than that of Mare Imbrium, it will be noted that, measured up to the outermost ring of mountains (that includes the Cordillera), maria Orientale (Fig. 38.3) and Imbrium (Fig. 5.1) are of comparable size. Unlike the case of Mare Imbrium, sub-radial lineaments are disposed around Orientale in roughly symmetric bundles (Figs. 38.1 and 38.2); and the central lineament of each of the four bundles follows one or other of the well-developed

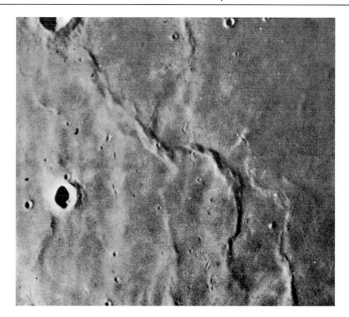

FIGURE 38.4 Wrinkle ridges near to Lambert, well away from the periphery of Mare Imbrium. [From the Photographic Lunar Atlas, Plate D3e (W). Edited by Gerard P. Kuiper. © The University of Chicago 1960, courtesy UC Press]

directions A and B of the local grid system simply because of the location of Mare Orientale in a crustal region of regularised, fractured terrain that was fractured prior to the impact.

Sinuous rilles (Fig. 38.5) occur mostly in the western maria of the nearside, particularly in the proximities of mare margins, and the rilles (Fig. 38.6) commonly change direction repeatedly. Sinuous rilles differ in origin from the normal, crater and arcuate types described in Section 36, although many are trench-like and similarly shallow relative to their widths. It is generally considered that they were cut out of the mare regolith and its substratum by the action of fluidised volcanic materials: Figs. 38.7 and 38.8. The fluids were erupted from characteristically circular to elongated-shaped crater-vents (Fig. 38.6) that are found at the wider, higher ends of the rilles. These vents, which have widths of up to 10 km, have been likened to the shape of a tadpole's head. Commonly, the crater-vents are disposed on hills such as wrinkle ridges. This association of some sinuous rilles with wrinkle ridges confirms that the rilles were produced by volcanic eruptions. Some of the sinuous rilles hug the feet of eminences (Fig. 38.6). Other flows that generated sinuous rilles were deflected in their courses by topographical features such as crustal fractures and terrain undulations that frequently follow the grid trends. In general, the flows must have been controlled by the slope of the terrain.

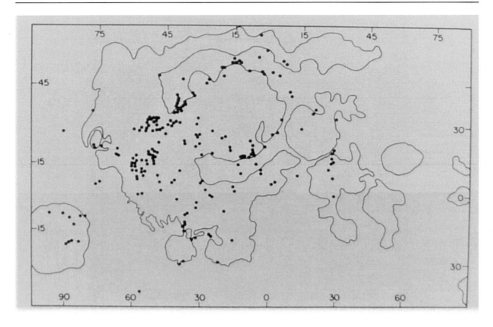

FIGURE 38.5 The distribution of lunar sinuous rilles. [J. Murray]

Downstream from their vents, sinuous rilles can run for hundreds of kilometres yet maintain nearly uniform widths. Under optimum conditions of solar illumination, some are seen to be flanked by banks. Eventually, these rilles become shallower and difficult to decipher. By contrast, many shorter sinuous rilles narrow downstream, in the fashion of a tadpole's tail.

Using Schröter's Valley (Fig. 38.9) as a prime example of a sinuous rille, W. Cameron proposed[55] an early explanation of some of the sinuous rilles when she discussed their origin in terms of a nuée ardente, or ash flow, which is a gas-charged, incandescent flow of volcanic ash and coarser particles.

On the Earth, nuées ardentes commonly derive from volcanic calderas and cool to form, generally, acidic deposits, of ash and larger pyroclasts, called ignimbrites. (Fig. 18.7). Of course, the conditions on the Moon were (and are) very different from those on Earth. On the Moon, outgassing of erupted materials, the extreme fluidity of the basic mare lavas, the porous nature of the regolith and the lower strength gravity field would, together, have led to distinct outcomes following the eruption of any kind of flow, including a turbulent ash-flow. So I thought it important to investigate the properties of lunar volcanic flows further, particularly after Strom and I found evidence[40] for a range of acidity in the lavas in and around Tycho.

In order to research further how lunar sinuous rilles might have been formed, I asked G. Hulme, a specialist in geophysical fluid dynamics, to work on the problems of turbulent, as well as of laminar, flows on the Moon and he found[56] that the erosive

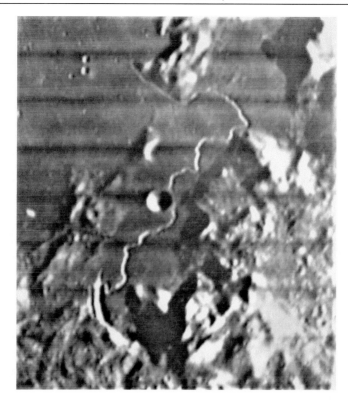

FIGURE 38.6 The sinuous rille Rima Hadley has its source vent at the Apennine front. Towards the rille's northern terminus it runs close to the feet of two mountains. [LO V, NASA]

power of a hot, turbulent lava could reasonably be expected to take out a swathe of the regolith by a scouring action combined, importantly, with melting and assimilation of the ground beneath the flow, thus deepening the channel. Hulme also found that, depending on the width of the channel, the volume rate of flow – and, therefore, the rate of eruption – would have needed to have been large in the case of long sinuous rilles and that, when steady conditions had set in, although there would have been loss of heat and possible consequent freezing over of the outgassing top and across any spillover levées at each side of the flow, there would have been no net heat loss to the ground. This property would have had the effect of maximising the length of the rille during the time that the eruption products continued to be supplied. Hulme's theory also explained why the width of even a long rille (Fig. 38.10) could maintain a nearly constant value: the reason was found in the lack of enough head to drive the flow laterally, together with the cooling that would occur along the edges of the flow. Had the eruption ceased suddenly, the residual turbulent part of the flow would have tended

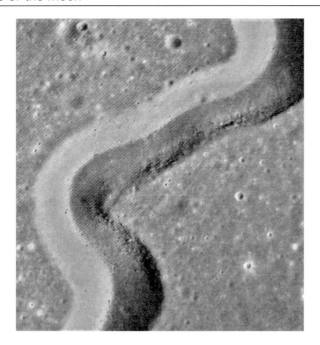

FIGURE 38.7   Part of Rima Hadley from orbit. Note the structural control of the rille. The original turbulent flow(s) exposed fine lineaments, in the upper walls of the rille, which intersect at about 90°, showing that this bend in the rille was influenced by the underlying "grid" structure. Note that, rather than following the wall crest, the fine lineaments cut across it. Ignore the diagonal stripes. [Apollo 15, NASA]

to empty the channel; and its contents would have been dispersed across the surface. Any further eruptions of turbulent lava could have deepened the channel.

The meandering of rilles is, in fact, evidence that they were generated by turbulent flow.[57] Also, I have found observational evidence that topography can generate sinuosity in cases when, for example, a flow traverses low undulations caused by lineaments that intersect orthogonally.

Estimates of the rheological (deformation and flow) characteristics of terrestrial lavas were in short supply in the early 1970s but the LPU's engineering geologist, H. Pinkerton, designed and developed an advanced rheometer which was constructed in steel by our technician G. Boulton. Pinkerton[87] was able to use his rheometer in the field to provide data which enabled him to estimate the viscosities of liquid lavas. This work was not without risk. Nevertheless, dressed in protective clothing, he succeeded in probing active basaltic lava flows on Mt. Etna; and he returned with our first measurements of their viscosities. These results provided an anchor point in our rheological

FIGURE 38.8   Many large blocks of rock have detached from the inner walls of Hadley rille and come to rest lower down, notably on the floor of the rille. The astronauts Irwin (pictured with the rover) and Wordern remarked on the apparent layering of the lavas seen in the upper parts of the walls. (A distinction has to be made between lava layering and structural lineamentation.) [Apollo 15, NASA]

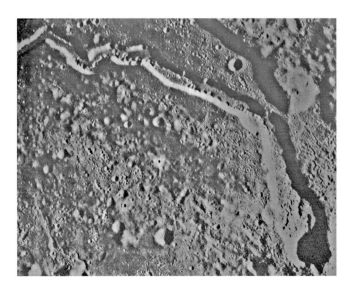

FIGURE 38.9   Schröter's Valley is a large, sinuous rille. [LO V, NASA]

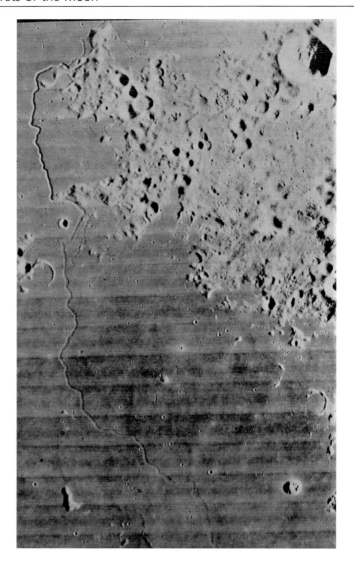

FIGURE 38.10 Rima Sharp is a long, sinuous rille that runs for several hundreds of kilometers (over 300 km are depicted here). Notice that the depths and widths of the rille change between the northernmost portion, in Sinus Roris, and the remainder of the rille, in northern Oceanus Procellarum. [LO IV, NASA]

studies of liquid lunar lavas. A review paper on lava viscosities was published by Chevrel[88] et al.

Looking at the extensive lava fields of the maria, Hulme[58] reasoned that some of these very fluid flows could have graded from near turbulent to fully turbulent, maintaining their high temperature of eruption along most of their length. Channels

FIGURE 38.11   One of the late flows in Mare Imbrium that has crossed the major mare ridge running NW from Lambert. My doctoral student, R. Todhunter, described morphology which indicated that late, viscous lavas were extruded from the top of the ridge after its broad banks had been formed and after the late flow that crossed those banks. The pointed shadow is cast by Mons La Hire. [Apollo 15, NASA]

from which the lavas overflowed to produce wide banks (Fig. 38.11) are in evidence in some flows. Several mare flows crossed wrinkle ridges: Todhunter[71] found evidence[36] for lava ponding on the south side of the ridge that was approached by flows lying between Lambert and La Hire (Fig. 38.11). There is the possibility that this prominent mare ridge continued to be built by extrusion after the flows in question crossed it.

Non-turbulent, and more viscous, laminar flows of mare lavas could have travelled through tubes (Fig. 21.5(a)) beneath a cooloing roof of lava that had crusted over, (possibly having attached itself to the levées of an original lava channel): this theory would fit the observations of the flow f2 that I described in Section 21. When the roof, consisting largely of underdense lava, covering a lava tube was thin, a chain of rimless craters, formed by collapse and drainage, could have been created, revealing the course of the tube. Much later, drainage of regolith might have been assisted by collapse of the underlying, underdense lava froth and by seismic activity or by small meteoroids that penetrated the regolith. In the cases when the craters of a chain are rimmed and elongated (Figs. 38.12 and 38.13), some eruptive mechanism such as fountaining,

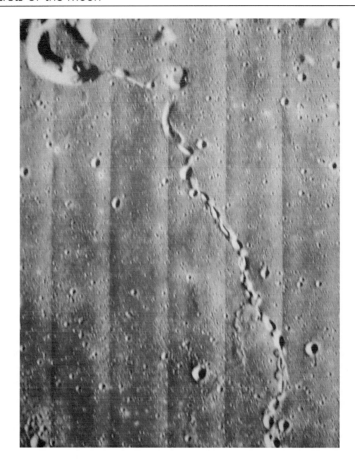

FIGURE 38.12   An unusual chain of elongated craters near to the western boundary of Mare Imbrium. Several of the elongated craters display rims that are proud of the surroundings. Other craters in the chain, which is probably fracture controlled, might have been caused by engulfment; but, in the case of the elongated craters with raised rims, pyroclastic activity might well have played a part in shaping them. [LO V, NASA]

might have been involved. Channels in which the lava flowed in laminar fashion would cool along the top, base and sides of a flow and, following Hulme's calculations, would not generate or maintain as much heat as in the case of a turbulent flow. This difference might explain the type of sinuous rille (Fig. 38.14) that degrades, downstream from the crater-vent, in the shape of a tadpole's tail. So there could be differences between the mechanisms of formation of different sinuous rilles. Even separate portions of a given rille or other lava flow might have been formed by different mechanisms, as in the case of a turbulent flow which becomes laminar.

FIGURE 38.13 Elongated craters, similar to some of those in Fig. 38.12, are seen in this example of joined, composite craters (built of cinders and lava flows) in the San Francisco Volcanic Field, northern Arizona. Here, the volcanic activity is known to be fracture-controlled. [G. Fielder]

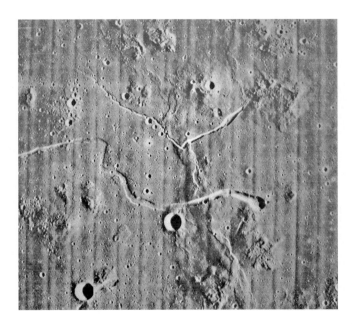

FIGURE 38.14 Tadpole-shaped rilles in Oceanus Procellarum near 14°N, 56°W. The circular crater immediately south of the larger rille is about 10 km in diameter and appears to be later than the rille. [LO V, NASA]

Further research on lunar sinuous rilles was completed[59] by Hurwitz et al. These authors were able to measure relevant parameters of Rima Prinz (near to Aristarchus), using the excellent combination of Lunar Reconnaissance Orbiter photographs along with the appropriate Lunar Orbiter altimeter measurements. They concluded that Rima Prinz was shaped by the thermal erosion of flowing lava.

Maria and Mascons

39

As Lunar Orbiter 5 passed, in its circum-lunar orbit, over certain lunar features, its radial acceleration fluctuated in an unexpected manner. This important development led to the discovery, by P. Muller and W. Sjogren,[60] of anomalies in the Moon's gravity field that could be explained only if some of the maria were underlain by unusual concentrations of mass, now known as "mascons". Mare Imbrium and Mare Orientale were found to harbour two of the biggest mascons. Further data on mascons were gathered through the later lunar satellites Clementine (NASA, 1994), Lunar Prospector (NASA, 1998) and Kaguya (2007), a Japanese spacecraft that released two sub-satellites in the process. That mission also led to a unique atlas of photographs.

The smaller maria (for example, Humorum and Nectaris) are associated with some sub-radial lineaments but they do not exhibit the strongly developed lineament bundles that characterise Imbrium and Orientale; possibly, some of the smaller maria were produced by less energetic impacts; but what all these maria do have in common is that they are sites of mascons.

Baldwin's contour map[61] of the central parts of the Moon's nearside indicated that all areas of lunabase occurring there are lower than the remaining areas of the nearside. In general, the sub-circular maria slope down towards their centres, whereas irregularly shaped areas of lunabase have more undulatory surfaces. More accurate maps of the Moon (Fig. 39.1), showing relative altitudes, were provided through the use of a laser altimeter aboard the Clementine probe and, in 2009, by NASA's Lunar Reconnaissance Orbiter (LRO). With Clementine, a useful advance came in 1994 with the production of an altitude map of the far-side of the Moon (Fig. 39.2). It proved that, not only did most of the farside rise to greater heights than the mean heights of the nearside but, remarkably, a non-mare sub-circular depression, presenting largely in the southern hemisphere of the Moon as the large, mauve patch in Fig. 39.2 and measuring roughly 2600 km in diameter - twice the size of Mare Imbrium – extended from the South Pole to the crater Aitken. And the GRAIL-LRO results showed that this huge depression – possibly the largest impact crater on the Moon – also coincided with a positive gravity anomaly.

Very early impacts that occurred in the building of the Moon from a circumlunar swarm would have struck the proto-Moon at low velocities (a few km per sec). If displaced asteroids had been involved, as the Moon grew to its present size, the impact velocities could have been appreciably larger (say, 10 km per sec). If cometary objects from beyond the orbit of Neptune had entered lunar space, impact velocities exceeding 50 km per sec could have pertained.

DOI: 10.1201/9781003181279-39

FIGURE 39.1   Relative altitudes of features on the Moon's near side deduced by differencing the orbital heights of the circumlunar Clementine satellite, tracked by radio, and the heights measured using Clementine's onboard laser device. The deepest parts of the Moon are shown in purple, the highest in orange through yellow. Lambert equal area projection. [From Plate 1 of The Clementine Atlas of the Moon, D.B.J. Bussey and P.D. Spudis. © D.B.J. Bussey and P.D. Spudis 2004. Reproduced with permission of the Licensor through PLSclear]

Deep basins beneath the present South Pole to Aitken depression and beneath the present lavas of maria Imbrium, Orientale and some other maria could have been created by high-velocity objects. Had that been so, most of each object would have vaporised; and the deep-focus explosions that they created would, essentially, have expelled most of the lunar crustal materials (as both melts and solids) from the Moon along fairly high-angle trajectories. The crustal rocks remaining in the basin floors would have been heated and shattered, allowing dense, mantle materials, freed by the reduction of overburden, to well up and cover the less dense crustal rocks, forcing

FIGURE 39.2   This is the corresponding Clementine map, showing an even larger range of altitude, on the far side of the Moon. Here, the areas of greatest altitude are shown in white and the lowest areas are in mauve through purple. Note the purple, central part of Mare Orientale near the lower right limb. The south pole to Aitken basin is clearly defined in mauve. Lambert equal area projection. [From Plate 1 of The Clementine Atlas of the Moon, D.B.J. Bussey and P.D. Spudis. © D.B.J. Bussey and P.D. Spudis 2004. Reproduced with permission of the Licensor through PLSclear]

them to sink. Later lavas entering the basins from a range of depths might have completed the process: in Mare Imbrium it is clear that late flows, many from sources beyond Mare Imbrium, were involved. For Mare Serenitatis, other lavas might have been forced up to the surface from depth. Calculating the gravitational effects that a similar, layered, model for Mare Serenitatis would have at a height of 100 km above the surface of the Moon, Hulme[62] obtained a close match to the positive gravitational anomaly deduced at the same height, over the same mare, by Muller and Sjogren. In the case of the South Pole to Aitken depression, on the farside of the Moon, the crust was possibly thicker than on the nearside and its boundary with the mantle was not, I suppose, disrupted enough to allow mantle magmas to be tapped to the extent found on the nearside. Cratering covered this vast area but, on the farside generally and possibly because of a thicker crust, contrasting with the flood lavas of the nearside, lava eruptions were restricted to the vicinity of craters where additional mechanical or thermal energy had been delivered.

Ghost Craters and Elementary Rings 40

A crater-like structure that appears to be a remnant of its former self may be referred to as a ghost crater or ghost ring. Seen at low resolution, Flamsteed P, diameter 112 km (Fig. 40.1), is characteristic of a large ghost that presents only some parts of a low, sub-circular wall, whereas Egede, 37 km across (Fig. 40.2), is an example of a smaller, sub-circular ghost ring with low walls. Like some ordinary craters, some ghosts have polygonal walls. But, unlike ordinary craters, ghost rings have walls that are narrower than those of the same-sized ordinary craters. The walls of the smaller ghost rings slope, inwards and outwards, by equal amounts and cover equal horizontal distances. A few ghosts have incomplete walls that appear to be extended by arcs of small craters, giving the impression that these small craters are volcanic and that, had they evolved further, the missing parts of the walls might have been constructed. The floors of ghosts tend to be at the level of the surroundings, so the word "crater" is inappropriate and the term "elementary ring" may be used as an option to "ghost ring".

The more readily recognized elementary rings are found in the lunabase and, judging by their reflectivities, their floors seem to be of mare-type lavas. Scores of probable elementary rings are distributed across the nearside of the Moon but a chart (Fig. 40.3) of their distribution[63] would indicate that they are scarce in those maria that are associated with mascons.

The elementary ring Wolf T, diameter 27 km (Fig. 40.4) is located in Mare Nubium, not far from Bullialdus (diameter 60 km). Wolf T is roughly hexagonal and most of its floor is as dark as the surrounding mare, although some parts of the floor are lighter-toned because they are crossed by either the sub-radial lineaments of Bullialdus or, possibly, the ray-elements of Tycho. An unnamed elementary ring (Fig. 40.5) immediately north of Aristillus, is crossed by a sub-radial bundle of lineaments that, at first glance, appear to have come later than the elementary ring (but see below). Similar cases are to be found in Lambert (diameter 30 km) and its association with a larger elementary ring (Fig. 40.6); and in Taruntius (56 km) and its association with a smaller elementary ring (Fig. 40.7) immediately to the south.

The traditional view of the origin of elementary rings is that they were once normal craters that were inundated by liquid mare lavas. The lavas melted large volumes of the walls of an original crater, leaving only some of the higher parts showing, while levelling the original crater floor. There are problems with that theory. L. Wilson (personal communication, 2019) found severe problems with the theory that the large

DOI: 10.1201/9781003181279-40

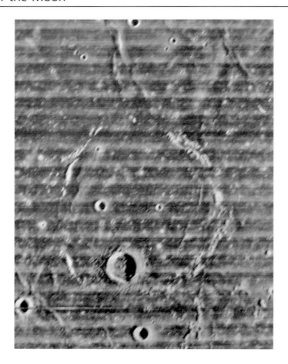

FIGURE 40.1   Flamsteed P, one of the larger ghost craters. Note that the NE wall appears to be linked to the wrinkle ridge to the north. [LO IV, NASA]

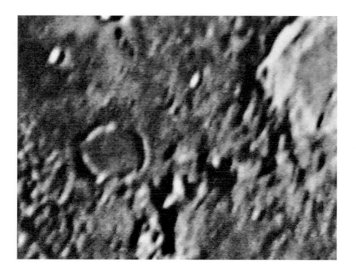

FIGURE 40.2   The ghost crater Egede. [Adapted from E. Whitaker, et al., Rectified Lunar Atlas, University of Arizona Press, 1963, Plate 7b (Y)]

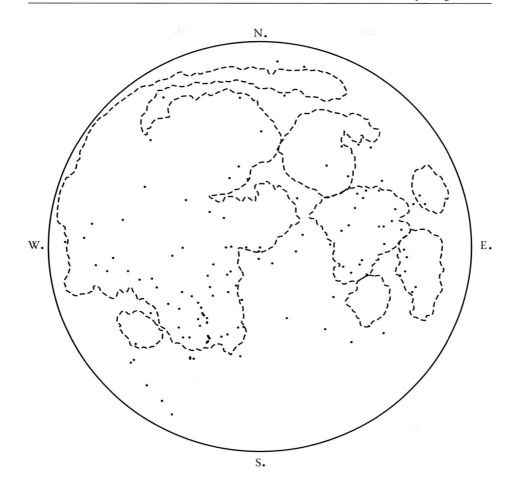

FIGURE 40.3   The distribution of elementary rings across the Moon's near side, shown in orthographic projection. [J. Guest]

volumes of a normal, large crater wall could be melted by mare lavas. Again, most large craters are enclosed by walls that differ in height around their rims. Melting of the walls by heating them from underneath is unlikely to leave an elementary ring with a smooth rim of uniform shape and height. Yet some of the elementary rings are of just that regular appearance. Rather than their taking the appearance of the truncated tops of the ringwall of an originally normal crater, the linear wall segments of even the large ghost Flamsteed P, seen at high resolution (Fig. 40.8) display notably rounded toes where they terminate at their contacts with the surrounding mare-type materials, presenting flow-like features. J. O'Keefe et al.[75] analysed these features and concluded that they were of acidic or intermediate composition, rather than the result of rock

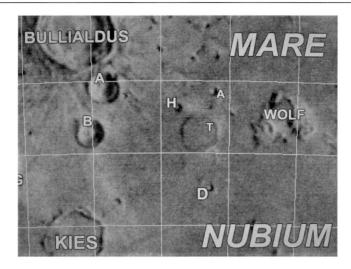

FIGURE 40.4   Wolf T, in Mare Nubium, is a polygonal ghost crater. [LAC 94, The Clementine Atlas of the Moon, D.B.J. Bussey and P.D. Spudis. © D.B.J. Bussey and P.D. Spudis 2004. Reproduced with permission of the Licensor through PLSclear]

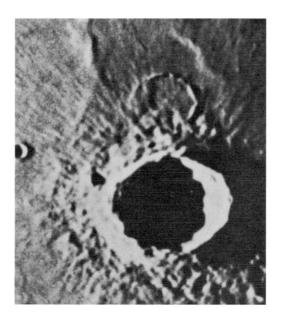

FIGURE 40.5   The elementary ring immediately north of Aristillus. Segments of the elementary ring that are nearest to the rim of Aristillus blend in to the trends of the sub-radial and cross-radial lineaments of Aristillus and tend to follow local grid directions. Indeed, all these local lineaments seem to be coeval. [From the Photographic Lunar Atlas, Plate D2e (L), in Gerard P. Kuiper. © The University of Chicago, 1960, courtesy UC Press]

FIGURE 40.6 The interfingering of ridge lineaments to the south of Lambert (30km diameter) where wall segments of an elementary ring that is nearly twice the size of Lambert confuse with the sub-radial and cross-radial lineaments that form a lattice pattern in Lambert's southern wall. [Apollo 15, NASA]

wastage, and that Flamsteed P was erupted as a ring dyke. The wall segments of Flamsteed P are lighter-toned than the lunabase. The crests of the wall-segments tend to parallel nearby lineaments such as linear rilles and the dyke-like segments of wrinkle ridges (see section 3); and there are direct physical links between the walls of Flamsteed P and regional wrinkle ridges (Fig. 40.1) that lie to the north of Flamsteed P and which, I have demonstrated, have originated by extrusion.

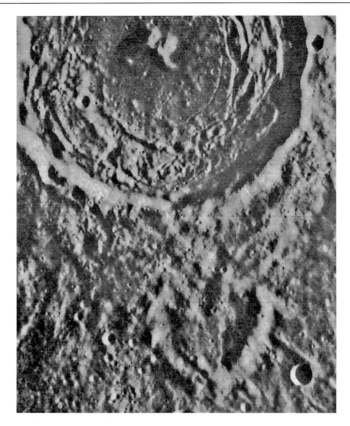

FIGURE 40.7 Taruntius (56 km in diameter, located at the northern edge of Mare Fecunditatis) is another crater with sub-radial lineaments that intersect and merge with those of an elementary crater that is about one third as big as, and immediately south of, Taruntius. [LO I, NASA]

Had the elementary rings Wolf T and the one abutting on Aristillus been formed by extrusions from simple ring fractures, the rings might possibly have formed even after the features that traverse their floors; but that is debatable.

The theory that incurs the tilting by subsidence into lava melts of certain other crater walls does, however, have supporting evidence in the many craters like Letronne, diameter 116 km (Fig. 40.9), in which there are normal, well-developed walls on the highland side but which, on the mare side, are lower and incomplete or totally missing. However, the melting problem expressed by Wilson must remain if partially-walled craters like Letronne once presented complete walls – unless we are dealing with much deeper and earlier sources of melting than those provided by near-surface, late mare lavas. Evidently, these mare lavas cannot have transferred enough

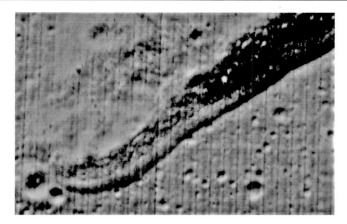

FIGURE 40.8   Flows that make contact with the local mare materials are from one portion of the walls of Flamsteed P. [Apollo 16, NASA]

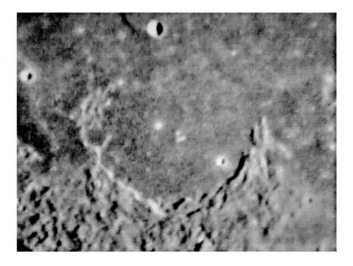

FIGURE 40.9   Letronne is a partially-walled crater which, if formed as an impact crater, has lost its walls on the side of the mare, probably when the materials beneath parts of the original crater carried enough heat to melt and assimilate them. [Adapted from E. Whitaker et al., Rectified Lunar Atlas, University of Arizona Press (1963), Plate 17b (M)]

heat to melt elementary ringwalls even as insubstantial as those of Wolf T when they were extruded. The hexagonal shape of Wolf T would demand a solid lava crust that was capable of sustaining fractures, as well as a crust that was cool enough to support, but not hot enough to melt, the low, extruded ring. If the foregoing analysis is correct, there must have been liquid lavas beneath the indurated mare crust when elementary rings similar to Wolf T were formed.

The Nature of the Lamont Complex **41**

Lamont (Figs. 41.1 and 41.2) is a double elementary ring in Mare Tranquillitatis. The inner ring is about 60 km across, the outer ring roughly 110 km across and, clearly, has been downfaulted on its western side between the craters Arago and Manners B. In order to confirm the faulting, and to elucidate the nature and form of the many wrinkle

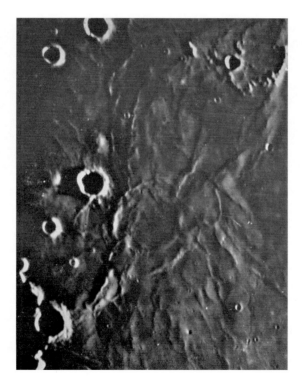

FIGURE 41.1 The elementary rings in the Lamont region of Mare Tranquillitatis. This sunrise photograph reveals the complex of mare ridges in a block of terrain that has been down-faulted. Major faults, dipping east, can be identified to the south of Arago (diameter 26 km). Two volcanic domes sit close to Arago. Compare this photograph with the corresponding sunset image of Fig 41.2. [Consolidated Lunar Atlas. G. Kuiper, E. Whitaker, R. Strom, J. Fountain and S. Larson. Pub: Lunar and Planetary Laboratory, University of Arizona, 1967]

DOI: 10.1201/9781003181279-41

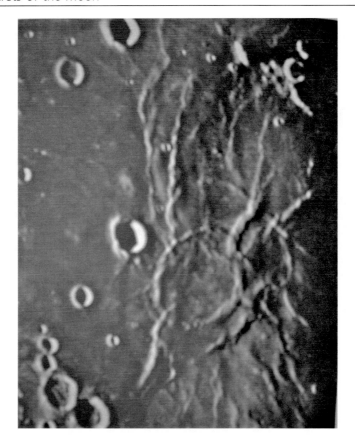

FIGURE 41.2   Late afternoon photograph of the Lamont region. With the low Sun now in the west, the faults to the south of Arago are conspicuous because of merging shadows. The tectonic and volcanic activity in this region might point to the presence of a batholith under Lamont. [Consolidated Lunar Atlas. G. Kuiper, E. Whitaker, R. Strom, J. Fountain and S. Larson. Pub: Lunar and Planetary Laboratory, University of Arizona, 1967]

ridges in the area, it is necessary to examine the region under very low solar lighting in both the morning and the evening. J. Guest and I[63] established the volcanic origin of the Lamont complex using these excellent photographs D5 and D11 of the USAAF's Consolidated Lunar Atlas. The reader will note the intimate connexions of the inner and outer rings of Lamont to the complex of wrinkle ridges in the area.

The major wrinkle ridge that leaves the eastern wall of Sabine (Fig. 43.1) to run in a north-easterly direction across the faults and, then, across the southern walls of the outer and inner rings of Lamont, links with orthogonal wrinkle ridges (particularly, those to the east of Lamont) as well as with north-to-south trending ridges (shown quite well to the north of Lamont). Control of the overall directions of the wrinkle ridges has been exercised by the underlying fractures of the grid system.

Polygonal elements are in evidence in the morphology of the walls of each of the elementary rings of Lamont, especially in the case of the inner one; and some small craters and hills continue the run of the low walls, notably in the southern part of the inner ring. There are chains of elongated ghost rings in the vicinity of the Lamont Complex and their inter-relationships, as well as their connexions with wrinkle ridges, known to be extrusives, and their interlocking with the Lamont rings are good reasons, I think, to reject the theory that these elementary rings are remnants of once pristine craters. Not far away, near to Arago, there are two good examples of mare domes (Figs. 41.1 and 41.2) which, in all probability, were formed by erupted lavas. Lamont itself is clearly the centre of much igneous activity where, it seems, extrusions of lava have been accompanied by a general subsidence of the area.

These basic judgments of the origin of the Lamont and other lunar elementary rings may be advanced by reference to some of the many ring features that occur on the Earth.

Terrestrial Ring Complexes and Their Origin

42

It is well known that the igneous activity in the Earth's upper crust can exhibit in the form of steep-sided volcanic cones (Fig. 42.1) built from lavas and pyroclasts; and that terrestrial volcanism can also present as shield volcanoes (Fig. 42.2), in which the slopes of their broad flanks are much less than the slopes of cones because shields are built from comparatively quiescent eruptions of low-viscosity, basic lavas. It is perhaps less known generally that terrestrial igneous activity can also commonly lead to ring complexes, so-called because, seen in plan, they may appear as one or more sub-circular rings or partial rings. Following significant erosional and denudational processes that operated for long periods of time on the Earth, these weathered ring complexes may still be viewed from above as arcs of circles or even as complete circles or ovals; and exposed cross-sections of the parts of them that were originally underground may sometimes be found. In less favourable cases, ground-penetrating radar can be used to add to our knowledge of their forms at depth.

Terrestrial ring complexes are fashioned by ring dykes and by cone sheets in which each sheet is generally narrower than a typical ring of a ring dyke. These types of volcanic intrusion can act in association. Examples of Tertiary ring complexes – those formed a few tens of millions of years ago – are to be found in the Scottish islands of Mull, Skye, Rhum (Rum), Ardnamurchan and Arran. More recent complexes are to be found at Slieve Gullion, Mourne and Carlingford, near to the east coast of Ireland. Many of these complexes outcrop as elongated features rather than as circular rings. The probable reason for the elongations is that crustal fractures exercise some control on both the dispositions of underlying magma chambers and on the final shapes of the outcrops.

All the complexes in Scotland and Ireland are underlain by swarms of dykes (Holmes[6]), generally trending SE–NW. Since the GRAIL mission to the Moon, we know that the lunar crust is, in similar fashion, permeated by dykes.

It seems that terrestrial ring fractures dip sub-vertically. Any dipping outwards at <90° to the horizontal (so that the rings would tend to decrease in radius on approach to the surface from beneath) would facilitate the dropping of the central block towards an underlying magma chamber. This action is referred to as "cauldron subsidence" and, in principle, liquid magmas at depth could be forced to rise up the ring fractures. However, the evidence from exposures in structures that have suffered different degrees of

DOI: 10.1201/9781003181279-42

FIGURE 42.1   Profile of Vesuvius from the forum, Pompei. [G. Fielder]

FIGURE 42.2   A windblown author standing on the rim of Mauna Loa at 4000 m above sea level, well above the tops of the cumulus clouds. Some of the black lavas within the caldera, measuring approximately 5 km × 3 km, contrast with the more oxidised lavas (spillovers of the past) where I am standing. Mauna Loa and Kilauea are still actively building this part of Hawaii. [Mr. Ellis]

denudation is that most ring fractures dip inwards. Under these conditions, ring fractures could open to allow the ascent of magmas if the central block were to be lifted by magmatic pressure from below. Interestingly, Rum (Holmes[6]) has a central uplift and, in plan, a set of sub-radial dykes that are reminiscent of the sub-radial fractures around large lunar craters. The Rum dykes would have been emplaced in a tensional regime caused by the uparching of the country rocks.

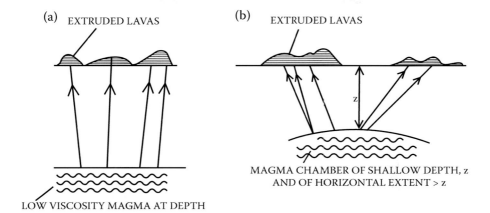

FIGURE 42.3   (a) Schematic sketch of ring-fracture dykes; (b) Schematic sketch of cone sheets. [G. Fielder]

FIGURE 42.4   Centres of terrestrial ring complexes plotted on a world map. [W. Elston]

Cone sheets are intrusions of magma that are shaped like the surfaces of cones having their apices pointing downwards, as in the case of Ardnamurchan. C. Moreau et al.[64] described a tectonic model of Palaeozoic (4×10^8 years ago) ring complexes in Central Africa and found that most of those rings, ranging from 1 km to 65 km in diameter, were nearly circular. Schematic cross-sections of ring dykes and cone sheets are shown in Fig. 42.3.

Some very interesting work on the dynamics of dykes and cone sheets has been reported by O. Galland et al.[65] The authors conclude that, for a given strength of host rock, ring dykes, rather than cone sheets, tend to form when the source of magma is deep and of low viscosity.

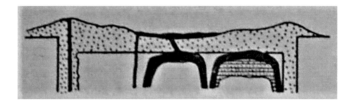

FIGURE 42.5 A vertical section of the 6km radius Buji ring complex, Nigeria. The first rhyolite to be erupted is shown stippled. The last rhyolite to be extruded, shown in black, formed a central deposit. [After R. Jacobson et al., Mem. Geol. Soc. Lond., No.1, 1958]

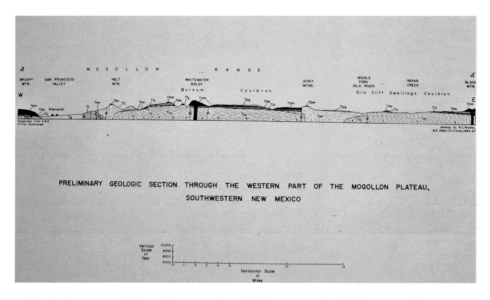

FIGURE 42.6 A vertical section A-A' through the western half of the Mogollon Plateau, southwestern New Mexico. The centre of this ring complex is at A', where basaltic extrusions formed "Black Mountain". The diameter of the ring is about 60 km (but possibly about 90 km for the whole disturbance). [W. Elston]

World wide, ring complexes are common. Several are discussed and listed in Table 4-5-1 of my book Lunar Geology;[21] but they offer only a small sample of the total number of such features on the Earth. W. Elston (private communication) plotted the positions of many more ring dyke complexes on a world map (Fig. 42.4). In a letter to me dated 11 March, 1968, Elston wrote "The enclosed compilation of known ring-dike complexes ... shows ... that they are far more abundant than the published literature would have us believe. The largest, in Siberia, has a long diameter of 180 km. The map shows about 330; and in some areas there are so many that they couldn't be shown separately. The data are, of course, most incomplete. The map doesn't include cauldrons or volcano-tectonic depressions in volcanic zones that show signs of recent activity. If these were shown, the number would approximately double". Elston noted that the Nigerian Province of ring structures extended from the Arabian Peninsula through North Africa; and that the same Province possibly cropped up in Brazil.

Cross-sections in vertical planes through the centres of terrestrial ring complexes are in short supply: three are reproduced in Lunar Geology[21], one of which (Fig. 42.5)

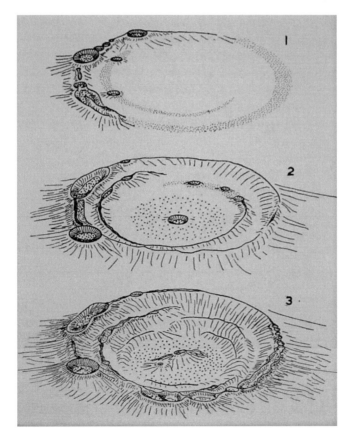

FIGURE 42.7   Possible development of a ring complex. [G. Fielder]

has a central extrusion feature. Research by Elston on his postulated ring complex termed the Mogollon Plateau, some 120 km in diameter, in south-western New Mexico showed that it had a central mountain of basalt, topped with a caldera nearly 5 km across, which had been extruded from a dyke that had cut through rhyolite. The western part of the ring complex is shown (Fig. 42.6) as a vertical section A-A', its centre lying at A'. To quote Elston, "the eastern half of the Mogollon Plateau looks pretty much like the western half … The stages of development are quite close to those illustrated on page 155 in … Lunar Geology. The tendency for ring walls to become younger towards the interior of the [Mogollon] structure is quite marked". The illustration referred to by Elston is reproduced here (Fig. 42.7). Again, in Africa the huge Bushveld Complex of basic rocks is, with an age of 2×10^9 years, only slightly younger than the Great Dyke of Southern Rhodesia, now Zimbabwe; and there might be an association between the two features. All these types of complex do seem to have made important contributions to the crust of the Earth. In plan, and in size range, the terrestrial ring dykes are superficially more like the larger lunar craters than are other forms of terrestrial volcano and it is natural to ask if, and to what extent, similar complexes have played a role on the Moon.

Are There Ring Dykes on the Moon?

43

Cone volcanoes, shield volcanoes and ring complexes on the Earth all draw on a source of magma that, commonly, forms, and resides in, a subterranean magma chamber at depths measured in kilometres below the free surface of the crust. When magmas can access conduits and find egress to the surface they can erupt as lavas and build structures of different shapes and sizes. Volcanoes differ in morphology because of the combined influences of various chemical and physical factors. For example, the chemical composition of a magma can vary, as can the temperature and pressure of the magma. Also, the physical conditions in the immediate environment of an eruption will influence the type and shape of volcanic feature: the shape of the magma chamber and the type and shape of the upward conduit can be important factors in determining the shape of the erupted landform. And, of course, there is the question as to whether an eruption takes place into an atmosphere or vacuum, or under water or regolith.

Given that terrestrial ring complexes were underlain by once-fluid magmas in the crust, it is evident that tidal forces on the rotating Earth, especially the early Earth, would cause these fluids to exert repetitive pressures on the rocks enclosing the magmas. With a roughly spherical magma chamber in a crust of uniform composition, for example, these pulsing pressures could, over time, lead to sub-circular crustal fracturing. This might explain why the ring complexes of the Earth are so old. Elongated magma chambers could have led to surface complexes that are themselves elongated.

Since ring dykes are so common on the Earth, I think that it would be rather surprising if their influence had not been felt on the Moon. However, in the case of the Moon, many of the aforementioned conditions are different from those of their terrestrial counterparts. With the present, synchronised Moon, a similar volcano-tidal process acting on any residual pockets of magma in the Moon's upper mantle would be less effective, than in the case for the Earth, as an aid to ring-fracturing. But, with the early Moon in free rotation and close to the Earth (and with the widespread grid fracturing discussed earlier), very strong tidal pressures on pockets of magma in the hot mantle, pushing up on a cool crust, would have generated conditions that might have induced ring fracturing. Magmas would have risen, preferentially, along the joints and fractures of the early grid system to create ring complexes that tended to be both sub-circular and polygonal.

DOI: 10.1201/9781003181279-43

With these possibilities in mind, I should like to consisder some further observational evidence that might be brought to bear on the problem of ring-fracturing and extrusion as a means of producing some of the lunar craters.

For me, one of the most interesting questions that arose from my observations of lunar craters was that of the interlocking of the ringwalls of some adjacent, or overlapping, craters. I first noticed the case of Sabine (diameter 30 km), in which a 44 km diameter partial elementary ring crosses the wall of Sabine (Fig. 43.1) at about 1° N, 20° E and appears to join the inner ring of Sabine. This relationship could not have occurred had the elementary ring been part of a former impact crater. Even one example is enough to prove that lavas were extruded from a ring fracture to form sub-circular walls. But there are other examples of this phenomenon. Lineaments that parallel the wall-segments of Clavius (diameter 245 km, Fig. 43.2) are to be found within the walls of the ringwall crater Porter (51 km) at about 56° S, 9° W. Would those segments have survived had Clavius, and then Porter, been formed purely as impact craters? I do not think so. The crater Nernst T (23 km) has been invaded, at 36° N, 97 °W, by a conspicuous linear extrusion (Fig. 43.3). The extrusion forms part of the ringwall of Nernst (125 km). This

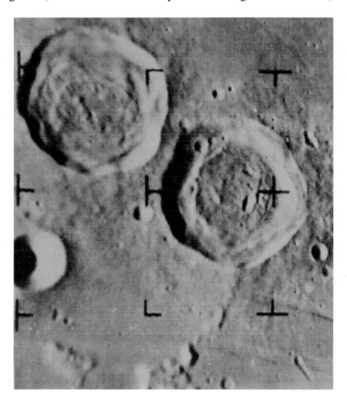

FIGURE 43.1   The interlocking craters Sabine (30 km) and the larger ghost to the south. An 11 km diameter crater, Schmidt, sits on the ringwall of this ghost ring, which might also interlock with Ritter, to the west of Sabine. It is helpful to examine the interlocking of these rings under reversed illumination (not shown here). [Ranger IX, NASA]

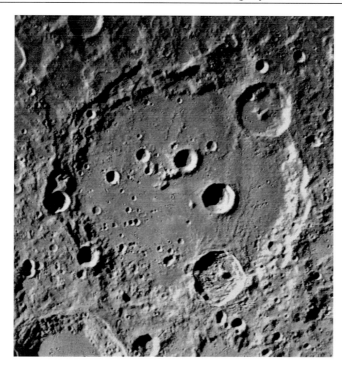

FIGURE 43.2 Interlocking wall segments of Clavius and its two largest ringwall craters Porter (on the northern wall of Clavius) and Rutherford (on the southern wall of Clavius). Systems A and B of the grid system are shown clearly on the floors of Porter and Rutherford, as well as in the areas to the NW and SE of Clavius. [LRO, NASA]

FIGURE 43.3 Nernst and its interlocking ringwall crater Nernst T. [LO IV, NASA]

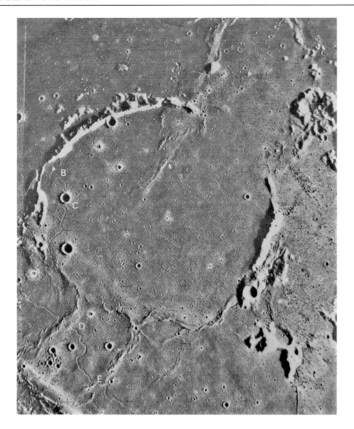

FIGURE 43.4 *A 70km diameter ghost crater in southern Oceanus Procellarum has walls that are undoubtedly linked to wrinkle ridges, their segments controlled in direction by underlying fractures of the grid system. Other large ghosts can be found immediately to the west. [Apollo 16, NASA]*

circumstance might have prevailed had the two craters been coeval, or had parts of them been generated within the same span of time; but not as a result of two impacts alone.

Other possible cases of the interfingering of parts of the walls of adjacent, or overlapping, craters may be found in the following examples: the ringwall craters of Avicenna (64 km) appear to interlock mutually at 40° N, 97° W; a ghost to the north of Kunowski (18 km) crosses the main crater's wall at 3° N, 32° W and the south wall of Bailly B (65 km) seems to overlap the wall of Bailly A (38 km), at 69° S, 61° W. There might well be many more interlocking craters for observers to discover.

The case of Flamsteed P (112 km in diameter), shown in Fig. 40.1, has already been discussed in Section 40. A similar, unnamed, elementary ring structure, 69 km in diameter (Fig. 43.4) is centred at 9°.5 S, 35°.1 W. Its walls are unquestionably linked, physically, to wrinkle ridges in the area, proving that the sub-circular walls of this elementary ring were formed by the eruption of volcanic materials. Together with other, similar cases this observation seems to support the idea that even the ringwalls of mature craters like Nernst might have been built – at least partly – by volcanic eruptions. Observations of oval craters situated in the tops of the ringwalls of many large lunar craters, (examine Clavius again, Fig. 43.2, to find examples of unnamed, craters in the ringwalls and note that some of these craters have their long axes in line with the local trend of the wall elements) add weight to the idea that volcanism was involved in the construction of some craters. And the lava flows already reported in the inner walls of Tycho, Copernicus and Aristarchus clearly contributed to the shaping of those walls. I make these comments not to argue against the initial impact origin of such large craters but, rather, to argue that craters were, not infrequently, significantly modified by later volcanism.

Finally, there are the interesting cases of arcuate crater-chains that appear to mark, or extend, a ring-fracture. An example is found in the rings of small craters (Fig. 43.5) near to Stadius (69 km), to the east of Copernicus: here, note especially the partial ring, larger than Stadius, that is centred at 11°.6 N, 16°.7 W. Although the arcuate crater-chains in this area are generally regarded as secondary impact craters associated with Copernicus, the small craters do have a tendency to define circles that might well be regarded as elementary rings; and this might be suggestive of fracture origins of both the elementary rings and these small craters. It should be noted that the most strongly developed of these small craters form a wavy crater-chain that, overall, has a trend that is paralleled by ridge lineaments near to Eratosthenes (58 km), at the western end of the Apennines, and these directions (close to the N–S direction) are known to promote features of tensional origin. There are similar cases to consider, such as a ghost crater that is adjacent to Mädler (27 km), in southern Mare Nectaris, where the walls of the ghost are marked, partly, by small craters.

A more traditional theory was proposed[66] by B. Warner, who noticed that, across the mare regions of the Moon's near-side, small, elongated craters were either single, elliptical craters, or closely adjacent pairs of craters in which the common wall was low or

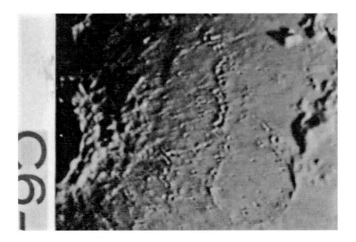

FIGURE 43.5 Small craters and the elementary ring Stadius, to the east of Copernicus. [From the Photographic Lunar Atlas, Plate D4f (P). Edited by Gerard P. Kuiper. © The University of Chicago 1960, courtesy UC Press]

missing. Examining the area to the east and south-east of Copernicus (one which includes the rings near to Stadius) he found a strong correlation between the longest axes of crater-pairs and the trends of systems A and B of the lunar grid; and he promoted the idea that these crater-pairs were elongated (looking rather like single, elliptical craters) because they followed underlying fractures. Nevertheless, Warner thought that the elongated craters were formed by secondary impacts, because they also appeared to be associated with the rays of Copernicus. E. Shoemaker proposed that the elongated craters around Copernicus were secondary impact craters but that their elongations were the result of elongated blocks of rock that had been detached and ejected from the Copernican impact site. I cannot accept that hypothesis, for I consider that, in the chaos of a major impact, it is unreasonable to suppose that such blocks could land with their major axes remaining closely aligned to one or other of the principal directions, A and B, of the grid system. I concur with Warner in that the elongations of the small craters are probably controlled by the grid fractures; but I am not sure that all of these craters around Copernicus are secondary impact craters. Some may be of a wholly internal origin, possibly energised by the Copernican impact. I think that further studies of the origins of these small craters are warranted.

On the whole, the evidence from interlocking ringwalls, rings that are physically linked to wrinkle ridges and to crater-arcs that extend probable ring-fractures, would, together, seem to support the hypothesis that there are, indeed, ring fractures on the Moon. Certainty is lacking in many cases and, in these cases, proof will need to be sought via further studies of high resolution imagery or on, or in the vicinity of, the Moon itself via research using ground-penetrating radar and gravimetry.

The Origins of Large Lunar Craters in General

44

With the opening up of the far side of the Moon, scientists have been presented with a vast inventory of craters of all sizes. If the proposed origin of the Moon is broadly correct, then craters would certainly have been produced by the low-velocity impact process during the terminal phases of the Moon's accumulation. Are those the impact craters that we see in the higher, non-mare areas of the Moon; or were the original craters partly covered, or even obliterated, by high-velocity objects from further afield? In either event, the result might have been an early surface saturated with craters, as shown, for example, in Fig. 18.9. A proportion of these craters might have been formed in a dualistic process involving impact and volcanism; still others, such as the ghost rings, might prove to be lavas that were extruded in the manner accepted for terrestrial ring complexes.

It now appears that the early, intense crater-forming episode was accompanied by the formation of the systems that are revealed as families of lineaments across the entire surface of the Moon. That grid system must have been initiated when the Moon was rotating freely. The crust cooled and the hot interior of the Moon continued to draw thermal energy from the dissipation of tidal friction and other sources of heat; and, as a consequence, the fractures tended to open. Deep basins were gouged out, initiating the formation of sub-circular maria, when large bodies collided with the Moon. Radioactivity gradually contributed more to the heating and melts rose up the fractures to form dykes. In cases in which the crust was thin enough, I propose that the deepest of the basins were partly filled with mantle materials, possibly having the potential to undercut and melt some of the large, early craters. In these regions, flood lavas poured out later in sequential episodes that covered many small, near-side craters and added to the mare fillings.

The marked height variations of the terrain in the lunar highlands, together with the undulatory nature of the lunabase, have made it difficult to deduce a simple geometrical shape of the entire Moon; but, following the work of Jeffreys,[80] it is generally agreed that the Moon had mostly solidified when it was in a state of free rotation and that the present, synchronous Moon has an irregular distribution of density along, and around, its earthward-pointing axis.[67] A hot Moon was, at first, unacceptable to Urey, who argued that the non-equilibrium shape of the Moon required its materials to have great strength. Yet the post-Apollo evidence was for large-scale melting that was

DOI: 10.1201/9781003181279-44

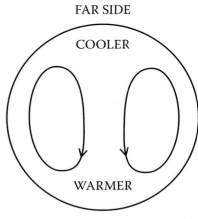

FAR SIDE

COOLER

WARMER

NEAR SIDE

FIGURE 44.1   The pattern of (hypothetical) first-order convection in the Moon. [G. Fielder]

needed to produce the suite of differentiated highland rocks. That process could have happened without homogenising the entire Moon. I think that the possibility of early convection in the Moon (Fig. 44.1) might provide a solution to these problems, particularly since first-order convection, rising along the earthward-pointing axis, might also explain why the lunar crust differs in its average thickness between the near and far sides.

While the opening and filling of the lunar crustal fractures would lead, in principle, to the egress of volcanic materials on both the near and far sides of the Moon, it might be expected that extrusion of the later, mare lavas would occur with more facility on the near side, with its thinner crust and greater heat content.[54] However, although extensive lava flows as important as those on the near-side are not in evidence on the Moon's far-side, numerous far-side craters are associated with volcanic phenomena, including lava floors, flows and lakes. Other authors[68,69] have discussed several of these craters and have argued that impacts created the melts. For reasons already given, I cannot, at present, find credence in these views; also, the authors' attempts to date different geological units are, I think, inadequate.

L. Wilson and J. Head[79] looked specifically at craters with floors that display a characteristic type of fracture pattern. Examples of large craters that display this kind of fracture pattern may be found in Vitello and in Humboldt (Fig. 44.2). Wilson and Head found an interesting way to explain this kind of fracturing in terms of volcanic sill emplacement beneath the craters, the intrusions arching their floors.

Again, we have seen how Tycho, once the epitome of a crater formed purely by impact, in fact, had a dualistic development. Although I had reasoned for a long time that its central mountains were volcanic, I had not expected to discover that volcanism had made such an important contribution to the present form of Tycho. As a process of modification, evidence for even more volcanism is readily found in and around many other craters. In particular, the so-called plateau-craters were apparently generated

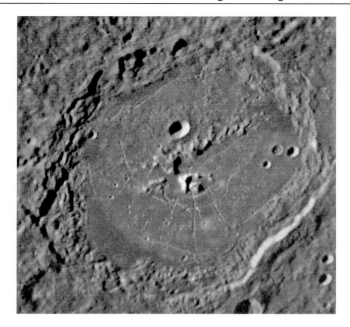

FIGURE 44.2   Humboldt, a 189 km diameter crater with fractured floor. [LRO, NASA/ GSFC/ Arizona State University]

when lavas welled up, within their walls, to create floors that are raised above the surroundings. The 84 km diameter crater Wargentin provides a key example, at 50°S, 60°W. Wargentin is now shown to advantage in a revealing photograph (Fig. 44.3) secured by NASA's Lunar Reconnaissance Orbiter. The last extrusions in Wargentin constructed wrinkle ridges on the indurated "plateau" of previously erupted lavas.

Examples of smaller plateau craters may be found in unnamed polygonal craters on the edge of the Altai scarp, at about 21°S, 21°E; on the equator at 10°E (near Lade, 55 km diameter); and at 24°S, 46°W, on the uplifted block of the fault bordering eastern Mare Humorum. These extrusions must have derived from deep fractures under the crater in question but, for any one impact crater, the degree of post-impact modification will have depended on the particular physical conditions in each locality. The gross lineaments around the Moon are inextricably linked to the ringwalls of large craters and maria and the shapes of initially circular craters were influenced – and occasionally transformed – by existing weaknesses and fractures in the lunar crust, by subsequent impacts and tectonic movements and, not infrequently, by volcanic processes.

By drawing on selected examples I have tried to show, in this short account, how different lunar features might have originated and developed. In particular, I have made recourse to the coarse, and fine, lineaments of the grid system to demonstrate how it can be used to aid our interpretation of lunar features and advance our knowledge of them. Nature is, indeed, complicated; and the study of lunar crater origins offers no exception. Diverse views of the origins of lunar surface features

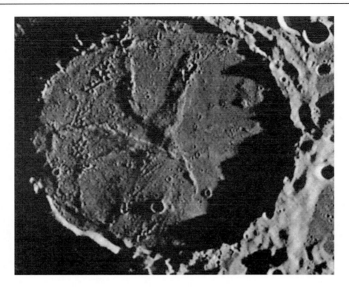

FIGURE 44.3 Wargentin, the 84 km diameter "plateau" crater, showing the late wrinkle ridges that were extruded through fractures in the lava-flooded floor after the lavas hardened. [LRO, NASA/GSFC/Arizona State University/Maurice Collins]

abound, partly because, I believe, preconceptions can dominate thoughts but, more importantly, because of the need to apply an interdisciplinary approach to selenology. Significant inventories of lunar data still await study and it can only be hoped that further explorations of the Moon will combine to resolve the many selenological issues that still require clarification.

Return to the Moon

45

Following the splashdown of the Apollo11 capsule that was carrying the first astronauts to return from the Moon in July 1969, I attended an extraordinary session in Houston, Texas, where Neil Armstrong and Buzz Aldrin (Fig 1.2) answered questions put to them by an excited audience. Earlier, Armstrong and Aldrin had laid out equipment, on the surface of Mare Tranquillitatis which, among other things, enabled on-going experimental results to be relayed to Earth-bound lunar scientists. That invaluable practice was continued through successive Apollo missions. Importantly, the Apollo11 astronauts also started a train of sampling by returning some 22 kg of the lunar surface rocks for analysis. Future sampling will be informed by the results deriving from all the Apollo landers as well as by results from various unmanned lunar orbital missions and by further photogeological studies such as those reported in this book.

In December 1972, Harrison Schmidt was the first scientist (specifically, a geologist) to work on the Moon during the Apollo 17 mission. After his safe return, he visited the United Kingdom and I was honoured to receive a handshake from him and converse with him in London. Exploring near to the landing site in the Taurus Mountains he had discovered a deposit of black and orange pyroclasts (glassy fragments) and later analysis proved them to be high in titanium and some 3.6 billion years old.

Schmidt[78] was keen to promote the notion of humans returning to the Moon in order to conduct further research, particularly that relating to the possibility of establishing a colony there. Among the essential needs of a lunar outpost would be supplies of electrical energy, water, air and food. In his book "Return to the Moon", Schmidt argued that power generation for a lunar base might employ the nuclear fusion of helium-3, itself derived as particles of the solar wind found to be embedded in the lunar surface materials, particularly those that are rich in an oxide of titanium known as ilmenite. Large parts of the surface of Mare Tranquillitatis and elsewhere are relatively high in titanium. Other useful minerals, such as potassium and sodium, have been found by NASA. A lunar orbital station has already been planned. Preparing a lunar surface outpost would be a great challenge for humanity and would be of assistance in attempts to further our knowledge of the Moon and its accessible mineral wealth, as well as by promoting more far-reaching projects to continue with the exploration of Mars and beyond.

In the immediate future, power could be generated on the Moon by utilising solar cells. The useful lifetime of a battery of solar cells on the Moon could be re-investigated by experimental testing, because of the potential degrading of such an

DOI: 10.1201/9781003181279-45

array by, principally, micro-impacts, hard radiation and the exposure of the array to extremely high and low temperature cycling. (In the absence of wind, an array of cells raised above the surface and placed away from human activity would be unlikely to acquire a significant coating of dust in the short term.) Electrical power from solar cells would be useful during lunar daytime and some could be stored for use at night. Later, power from the sunlit far side could, in principle, be relayed to the night-time near side.

Decades ago, H. Urey[1] reasoned that condensed, volatile substances might be present in depressions near the poles of the Moon, where the Sun never shines. G. Kuiper was one of the first to reason that water-ice, specifically, might be found in the permanently shadowed parts of craters located in lunar polar regions. His thesis was given substantive support following more recent investigations using circum-lunar probes. Although transporting ice-rich material, or manufactured water, from a polar station to a station at lower latitudes would pose serious problems, the volcanic components of rocks returned in the Apollo programme are known to have contained some water and it now seems that, even under a high Sun, the regolith (although considerably drier than the driest terrestrial desert) might be trapping quite small concentrations of water-ice that could possibly, through bulk processing of the re-golith, be made available to astronauts. Heat exchange systems might be harnessed, if necessary, in order to maintain adequate night-time temperatures in living quarters. Test drilling of boreholes could be of use in assessing the potential of selenothermal (geothermal in application to the Moon) heat for night-time use. In daytime, solar radiation could be focussed on rocks to generate water from which oxygen might be extracted by electrolysis. Zwicky[89] outlined a scheme to meet essential requirements. Oxygen bound chemically to the metallic oxides in the regolith might also be released for both life support and rocket fuel. A NASA scheme for an early lunar base is described by Vaniman et al.[92]

A lot depends on finding a practicable method of producing and storing liquid water. Given water, trials of novel methods of in situ food production, such as by the use of hydroponics, could be initiated. NASA has already ascertained that some seeds will develop and grow in lunar soil returned to Earth. On the Moon, attempts will surely be made to cultivate some plants for food. Experiments might be started in a part-pressurised house, using recycled carbon dioxide and accessed via an "air" lock, constructed just beneath the surface and covered with a layer of regolith to protect against radiation and micrometeoroids. The plants' house could be heated and lit, as required, and water administered, to see if any plants might grow in a useful way. Artificial fertilisation could be trialled in the future.

Radiation from the Sun and stars is variable and can be harmful to life. For the protection of astronauts in space, and on the Moon, I envisage the establishment of a system of "weather" forecasting to issue warnings of hard radiation hazards from major solar coronal mass ejections that are directed towards the Earth-Moon system and from bursts of hard radiation emanating in other parts of the Galaxy. Safe "win-dows" for visits to the Moon might be chosen by taking regard of observations gathered by a satellite in orbit around the Sun, combined with more general, relevant astronomical observations. For people wishing to stay on the Moon for longer periods, new methods of body protection from both daytime radiation and night-time cold and radiation might be organised: for example, like the plants' house, living quarters might be covered with an appropriate thickness of regolith.

A number of nations is now (2021) planning further exploration of the Moon with a view to constructing a manned outstation there. More than one company is actively testing capsules that are designed to transport astronauts and supplies not just to the International Space Station but beyond it, to the Moon and back. Through the next decade, I expect that we will discover the usefulness of a station orbiting the Moon, possibly to facilitate onward travel to Mars and, later, a base for lunar science and for regulated lunar-based industry.

With regard to the need for further, specifically lunar surface, studies I have raised a number of academic questions in this book that lunar scientists, now and in the future, might wish to investigate. High-resolution orbital photography has already proved its worth. More complete photo-coverage of the craters Tycho, Aristarchus, Copernicus (sections 25 through 35), Jackson, Proclus and Giodano Bruno (section 34), as well as of some possible lunar ring-complexes (sections 40 through 43), could lead to clarification of the origin of these large craters. On the Moon, the use of ground-penetrating radar might reveal hidden dykes and discover the first lunar ring-dyke.

Much man-made equipment now resides at known sites on the Moon and has been exposed to the damaging effects of micrometeoroids and solar radiation for different, known periods of time. Averaged counts of the microcraters that have accumulated on parts of all that equipment could be used as an independent method of estimating the present impact flux. A useful start to the process of examining the damage to abandoned equipment was made when, in November 1969, astronauts C. Conrad Jr. and A. Bean, from the Apollo 12 lunar lander, visited the Surveyor 3 vehicle that had soft-landed some two and a half years earlier and was (by careful management) less than 200m distant from the Apollo 12 module. In future times, mission planners might consider a programme to retrieve suitable parts of equipment landed earlier in order to determine a mean impact rate. That result could be compared with the rate I adopted (section 17) and the new result used to re-evaluate the present intensity of lunar surface erosion and denudation.

Much more geological sampling and rock-analysis should rank as a priority of further manned missions to the Moon. Is there evidence, in the vicinity of Surveyor VII, for base-surge deposits? And were the fractured blocks of Fig. 16.11 formed in situ? Sampling of proposed impact melts that occur in association with a number of craters of sizes less than some 20 km (section 31) might settle the issue of the origin of these deposits. Importantly, wide ranging tests for water should be prioritised.

Sampling of the flow f2 (sections 21 through 24) could be used to determine both the compositions and the ages of specimens drawn from several morphologically different types of crater on the flow. Samples of the ghosts and their associated, well-formed companion craters of section 40, would shed light on the age problems that I raised in the text. Similarly, the walls of elementary rings could be sampled for composition and age and compared with the same parameters of their associated mare ridges (section 41). Close-up examination of double craters (sections 22 and 23); the assessment of the difference between the compaction of the regolith that covers the flow f1 and that that covers f2; and the sampling of these flows with the objective of determining their respective ages should deliver clarity on several issues.

Field studies and analyses of specimens drawn from the central mountains of a large crater (sections 25 through 33) might help to resolve a major issue concerning the nature and origin of these features. Aristarchus, where ilmenite and radon have been detected, might be a good place to start.

In situ mineral searches might be conducted in geologically promising areas such as the recognisable volcanic sources of lava flows (section 21); in the volcanic source-craters of lunar rilles (section 38); on the late flows and floor features of Aristarchus or Tycho (section 27); on the floors and walls of sinuous rilles (section 38 and Fig. 38.9); and across swathes of Mare Tranquillitatis or Mare Crisium, with the aim of identifying the richest concentrations of ilmenite.

In closing, I express my hope that, however difficult to implement, laws that are acceptable to the international community will be agreed in order to manage future developments on the lunar surface. Perhaps any future lunar quarrying, or mining, will be regulated so as to protect the relatively unspoilt environment of our Moon. Yet the Moon does now preserve landers and other equipment at sites of special scientific interest; so consideration might also be given to maintaining important historical markers.

A technically difficult, but hopefully very interesting, future lies ahead.

References

1. Urey, H.C., *The Planets*, Oxford Univ. Press, 1952.
2. Baldwin, R.B., *The Face of the Moon*, Chicago Univ. Press, 1949.
3. Bussey, B. and Spudis, P.D., *The Clementine Atlas of the Moon*, Cambridge Univ. Press, 2004.
4. Spurr, J.E., Geology Applied to Selenology, Vol. 1 (1944); Vol. 2 (1945); Vol. 3 (1948); Vol. 4 (1949), Lancaster, PA.
5. Moore, P., *Guide to the Moon*, Eyre and Spottiswoode, 1953.
6. Holmes, A., *Principles of Physical Geology*, Nelson, 1944, reprinted 18 times, 1965.
7. Anderson, E.M., *The Dynamics of Faulting*, Oliver and Boyd, 1951.
8. Fielder, G., Measurement of the Profile of a Lunar Wrinkle Ridge, *M.N.R.A.S.*, **118**, 547–550, 1958.
9. Kuiper, G.P., in Alperin and Gregory (Ed.), *Vistas in Astronautics*, Pergamon Press, 1959.
10. Fielder, G. and Kiang, T., The Segmental Structure of Wrinkle Ridges and the Lunar Grid System, *Observatory Mag.*, **82**, 8–9, 1962.
11. Fielder, G., The Measurement of Lunar Altitudes by Photography – II. Some Measurements of the Lunar Straight Wall, *Planet. and Space Sci.*, **9**, 929–938, 1962.
12. Fielder, G., Topography and Tectonics of the Lunar Straight Wall, *Planet. and Space Sci.*, **11**, 23–30, 1963.
13. Gilbert, G.K., The Moon's Face, *Bull. Phil. Soc. Wash.*, **12**, 241–292, 1893.
14. Fielder, G., Lunar Tectonics, *Quart. J. Geol. Soc. Lond.*, **119**, 64–94, 1963.
15. Darney, M., Le system Imbrien, *Bull Soc. Astron. de France*, **47**, 452–457, 1933.
16. Marsden and Cameron, ed's., *TheEarth-MoonSystem*, Plenum Press, 1966.
17. Fielder, G., The Contraction and Expansion of the Moon, *Planet. and Space Sci.*, **8**, 1–8, 1961.
18. Fielder, G., Strike-slip Faulting in the Vaporum Region of the Moon, *Quart. J. Geol. Soc. Lond.*, **120**, 275–281, 1964.
19. Fielder, G. and Jordan, C., Selenological Implications drawn from the Distortions of Craters in the Hipparchus Region of the Moon, *Planet. and Space Sci.*, **9**, 3–9, 1962.
20. Arthur, D.W.G., and Whitaker, E.A., in Kuiper, G.P..(Ed.), *Orthographic Atlas of the Moon*, Univ. Ariz. Press, 1960.
21. Fielder, G., *Lunar Geology*, Lutterworth Press, London, 1965; reprinted by Dufour Editions, USA, 1967.

22. Heiken, G.H., Vaniman, D.T., and French, B.M. (Eds), *Lunar Sourcebook*, Cambridge Univ. Press, 1991.
23. Fryer, R.J., PhD. Thesis, Univ. Lancaster, U.K., 1973.
24. Alter, D., The General Background of the Lunar Surface, *Pubs. Astr. Soc. Pacific*, **75**, 30–35, 1963.
25. Gash, P.S.J., PhD. Thesis, Univ. Lancaster, U.K., 1973. See also: Tidal Stresses in the Moon's Crust, Modern Geol., **6**, 211–220, 1978.
26. Taylor, S.R., *Solar System Evolution*, Cambridge Univ. Press, reprinted 2005.
27. Hartmann, W., et al (Eds), *Origin of the Moon*, Lunar and Planetary Inst., Houston, 1986.
28. Fielder, G., Guest, J.E., Wilson, L., and Rogers, P.S., New Data on Simulated Lunar Material, *Planet. and Space Sci.*, **15**, 1653–1666, 1967.
29. Fielder, G., in Runcorn, S.K., *Mantles of the Earth and Terrestrial Planets*, Interscience/Wiley and Sons, 1967.
30. Fielder, G., (Ed), *Geology and Physics of the Moon*, Elsevier Pub. Co., 1971.
31. Fielder, G., Erosion and Deposition on the Moon, *Planet. And Space Sci.*, **11**, 1335–1340, 1963.
32. Fielder, G., Some Aspects of Some Lunar Ray Systems and the Discrete Nature of the Rays, *J. Brit. Astron. Assoc.*, **66**, 223–229, 1956.
33. Fielder, G., Tests for Randomness in the Distribution of Lunar Craters, *Mon. Not. Roy. Astr. Soc.*, **132**, 413–422, 1966.
34. Fielder, G., and Marcus, A., Further Tests for Randomness of Lunar Craters, *Mon. Not. Roy. Astr. Soc.*, **136**, 1–10, 1967.
35. Fielder, G., Fryer, R.J., Titulaer, C., Herring, A.K., and Wise, B., Lunar Crater Origin in the Maria from Analysis of Orbiter Photographs, *Phil. Trans. Roy. Soc., A*, **271**, 361–409, 1972.
36. Fielder, G., and Wilson, L. (Eds), Volcanoes of the Earth, *Moon and Mars*, Elek Science, Lond., 1975.
37. Fielder, G., and Fielder, J., Lava Flows in Mare Imbrium, *Boeing Sci. Res. Labs Doc.D1-82-0749*, 1–36, 1968.
38. Oberbeck, V.R., and Quaide, W.L., Experimental Impact Ctaters formed in Two-layered Media, *J. Geophys. Res.*, **72**, 4697, 1967.
39. Miethe, A., and Seegert, B., Uber qualitative Verschiedenhieten des von den einzelnen Teilen der Mondoberflache reflektierten Lichtes, *Astron. Nach.*, **188**, 9–12; 239–246; and 371–372, 1911.
40. Strom, R.G., and Fielder, G., Multiphase Eruptions Associated with the Lunar Craters Tycho and Aristarchus, *Communication No.150 of the Lun. and Planet. Lab.*, Univ. of Arizona, 1970.
41. Shorthill, R.W., Borough, H.C., and Conley, J.M., Enhanced Lunar Thermal Radiation During a Lunar Eclipse, *Publs. Ast. Soc. Pacific*, **72**, 481–485, 1960.
42. Pettengill, G.H., and Henry, J.C., Enhancement of Radar Reflectivity Assocoiated with the Lunar Crater Tycho, *J. Geophys. Res.*, **67**, 4881–4885, 1962.
43. Chapman, R.G., and Fielder, G., On the Central Peaks of Lunar Craters, *Observ. Mag.*, **84**, 23–27, 1964.
44. Baldwin, R.B., *A Fundamental Survey of the Moon*, McGraw-Hill, 1965.
45. King, E.A., *Space Geology*, Wiley and Sons, 1976.
46. Hulme, G., Generation of Magma at Lunar Impact Crater Sites, *Nat.*, **252**, 556–558, 1974.
47. Short, N.M., *Planetary Geology*, Prentice-Hall, 1975.
48. Andrews-Hanna, J.C., et al, Ancient Igneous Intrusions and Early Expansion of the Moon revealed by GRAIL Gravity Gradiometry, *Science*, **339**, 675–678, 2013.
49. Fielder, G., A Theory of the Origin of Lunar Rilles, with Particular Reference to the Ariadaeus-Hyginus Rille-System, *J. Internat. Lun. Soc.*, **1**, 166–175, 1960.

50. Fielder, G., and Warner, B., Stress Systems in the Vicinity of Lunar Craters, *Planet. and Space Sci.*, **9**, 11–18, 1962.

51. Fielder, G., Selected Lunar Observations made at the Pic-du-Midi Observatory in 1956 and 1959, *J. Brit. Astron. Assoc.*, **71**, 207–214, 1961.

52. Kalinyak, A.A., and Kamionko, L.A., in Kopal, Z., and Mikhailov, Z.K., *The Moon*, Academic Press, 1962.

53. Fielder, G., A Study of the Valley System Radial to Mare Imbrium, *J. Brit. Astron. Assoc.*, **66**, 26–31, 1955.

54. Fielder, G., Nature of the Lunar Maria, *Nat.*, **198**, 1256–1260, 1963.

55. Cameron, W., An Interpretation of Schroter's Valley and other Lunar Sinuous Rilles, *J. Geophys. Res.*, **69**, 2423–2430, 1964.

56. Hulme, G., Turbulent Lava Flow and the Formation of Lunar Sinuous Rilles, *Mod. Geol.*, **4**, 107–117, 1973.

57. Yalin, M.S., *Mechanics of Sediment Transport*, Pergamon, 1972.

58. Hulme, G., and Fielder, G., Effusion Rates and Rheology of Lunar Lavas, *Phil. Trans. Roy. Soc. Lond., A*, **285**, 227–234, 1977.

59. Hurwitz, D.M., et al, Origin of Lunar Sinuous Rilles: Modeling Effects of Gravity, Surface Slope, and Lava Composition on Erosion Rates During the Formation of Rima Prinz, *J. Geophys. Res. – Planets*, **117**, E00H14, 15pp, 10.1029/2011JE004000, 2012.

60. Muller, P., and Sjogren, W., Mascons: Lunar Mass Concentrations, *Amer. Assoc. for the Advanc. of Sci.*, **161**, 680–684, 1968.

61. Baldwin, R.B., *The Measure of the Moon*, Univ. Chicago Press, 1963.

62. Hulme, G. Mascons and Isostasy, Nat., **238**, 448–450, 1972.

63. Guest, J.E., and Fielder, G., Lunar Ring Structures and the Nature of the Maria, *Planet. and Space Sci.*, **16**, 665–673, 1968.

64. Moreau, C., et al, Palaeozoic Ring Complexes in Central Africa, *Tectonophys.*, **234**, 129–146, Elsevier, 1944.

65. Galland, O., et al, Dynamics of Dikes Versus Cone Sheets in Volcanic Systems, *J. Geophys. Res. (Solid Earth)*, **119**, 6178–6192, 2014. [10.1002/2014JB011059.]

66. Warner, B., Stresses in the Surface of the Moon, *J. Brit. Astr. Assoc.*, **71**, 388–395, 1961.

67. Fielder, G., *Structure of the Moon's Surface*, Pergamon Press, 1961.

68. Howard, K.A., and Wilshire, H.G., Flows of Impact Melt at Lunar Craters, *J. Res. U.S. Geol. Surv.*, **3**, 237–251, 1975.

69. Hawke, B.R., and Head, J.W., Impact Melt on Lunar Crater Rims, pp. in 815–841, *Impact and Explosion Cratering*, Pergamon Press, 1977.

70. Fielder, G., Ray Elements and Secondary-impact Craters on the Moon, *Ap. J.*, **135**, 632–637, 1962.

71. Todhunter, R., PhD Thesis, Univ. of Lancaster; see also reference 36.

72. Darwin, G.H., Tidal Friction and Cosmogony, *Scientific Papers*, **2**, Cambridge Univ. Press.

73. Wood, C.A., and Collins, M.J.S., *21st Century Atlas of the Moon*, West Virginia University Press, 2013.

74. Philip's Moon Map, New Edn., 2018.

75. O'Keefe, J.A., Lowman Jr., P.D., and Cameron, W.S., Lunar Ring Dikes from Lunar Orbiter I, *Science*, **155**, 77–79, 1967.

76. Hayne, P.O., et al, Global Regolith Thermophysical Properties of the Moon From the Diviner Lunar Radiometer Experiment, *J. Geophys. Res: Planets*, **122**, 2371–2400, 2017. 10.1002/2017 JE005387.

77. Elston, W., et al, Non-random Distribution of Lunar Craters, *J. Geophys. Res*, **76**, 5675–5682, 1971.

78. Schmidt, H., *Return to the Moon, Copernicus Books.* in Association with Praxis Publishing, Ltd., 2006.

79. Wilson, L., and Head, J.W., Lunar floor-fractured craters. Modes of dike and Sill Emplacement and Implications of Gas Production and Intrusion Cooling on Surface Morphology and Structure, *Icarus*, **305**, 105–122, 2018.
80. Jeffreys, H., *The Earth: Its Origin, History and Physical Constitution*, 4th edn., Cambridge Univ. Press, 1962.
81. Neish, C.D., et al, Global Distribution of Lunar Impact Melt Flows, *Icarus*, **239**, 105–117, 2014.
82. Fielder, G., Zones of Plasticity around Lunar Craters, *The Observatory*, **82**, 196–204, 1962.
83. Fielder, G., The Measurement of Lunar Altitudes by Photography – I. Estimating the True Lengths of Shadows, *Planet. And Space Sci.*, **9**, 917–928, 1962.
84. Gold, T., The Lunar Surface, *Mon. Not. Roy. Astr. Soc.*, **115**, 585–604, 1955.
85. Kuiper, G. (Ed.), *Photographic Lunar Atlas*, Chicago University Press 1960.
86. Strom, R.G. et al., The Inner Solar System Cratering Record and the Evolution of Impactor Populations, *Res. in Astron. and Astrophys.*, **15**, No. 3, 407–434, 2015.
87. Pinkerton, H. and Sparks, R.S.J., Field Measurements of the Rheology of Lava, *Nature*, **276**, 383–385, 1978.
88. Chevrel, M.O., Pinkerton, H., and Harris, A.J.L., Measuring the Viscosity of Lava in the Field: A Review, *Earth-Science Reviews*, **196**, 102852, 01.09.2019.
89. Zwicky, F., Physics and Chemistry on the Moon, pp. 1–25 in Malina, F.J., (Ed.), *Research in Physics and Chemistry*, Pergamon Press, 1969.
90. Alter. D., *Pictorial Guide to the Moon*, T.Y. Crowell Company, 2nd edition, 1967.
91. Holmes, A., *Principles of Physical Geology*, Nelson, 1965.
92. Vaniman, D., French, B., and Heiken, G., Chapter 11, pp. 633–654, in Heiken, Vaniman, and French, *Lunar Sourcebook: A User's Guide to the Moon*, CUP, 1991.

Glossary

ACIC: Aeronautical Chart and Information Center, United States Air Force.

Angle of repose: the acute angle between the horizontal and the sloping face of a pile of particulate matter that has come to rest naturally, under gravity.

Anorthosite: a basic igneous rock, rich in plagioclase.

Base surge: a great volume of incandescent materials (gases, rock fragments and blocks) that is propelled away from an explosion centre such as that created by a major impact or explosive volcanic process.

Batholith: a large, intrusive mass.

Brecciation: a process in which rocks are smashed to become fragmental and pressured to become metamorphosed.

Caldera: crater formed by either ring-fracturing and downfaulting and/or by engulfment incident on the withdrawal of lava or magma.

Centripetal force: force directed inwards, tending towards a centre.

CSNA: China National Space Administration.

Coronal mass ejections: very energetic, magnetic solar events in which atomic and sub-atomic particles such as protons are discharged from the polar regions of an active Sun.

Cohesive strength: a measure of the strength that a rock, or other medium, has in resisting a change of shape.

Composite fault: in the most general case, the movement of faulted rocks may be resolved into three mutually perpendicular directions. Commonly, one component of movement dominates but, in a composite fault, other components can be recognised; and the description of the fault can change from being principally of one type at one location to being principally of another type elsewhere.

Conservation of angular momentum: consider a point mass, m, rotating with tangential velocity v in the plane of this paper and in a circle of radius r. The angular momentum of the mass m can be regarded as the moment of its instantaneous linear momentum, mv, about the (vertical) rotation axis; that is, mvr. In an isolated system, the total angular momentum is conserved.

Couple, gravitational: two parallel, not collinear, equal gravitational forces acting on a body at different points but in opposite directions.

Crater, double: used here to indicate one small crater disposed, frequently concentrically, within another.

Crater, elementary or ghost: a crater of low relief, or one with parts of its ringwall missing.

Crateriform: shaped like a crater or, if in reference to a rille, one housing a chain of crater shapes.

Crater, plateau: a crater that has suffered substantial infilling by fluid lava.

Crater, secondary: a smaller crater formed when an ejectum from a larger crater impacts the terrain.

CSA: Canadian Space Agency

Differentiation (of igneous rocks): the natural separation of chemically distinct components of a magma.

Dihedral angle: the minimum angle bounded by two inclined planes.

Downthrow of fault: the terrain, on one side of a dip-slip fault, that has been displaced downward relative to the upthrow.

Dyke (Amer. Dike): sub-vertical igneous intrusion (can appear as an outcrop) of sheet form.

Ecliptic: the plane in which the Earth orbits the Sun.

Elementary rings: the term is used here to denote those ringwalls that were probably produced wholly by extrusion.

Endocrater: a crater that originated by internal action.

Endogenic: formed by internal action.

En-echelon (in geology): a surface arrangement of a series of linear features that are mutually parallel but inclined somewhat to the overall trend of the principal fault.

ESA: European Space Agency.

Exogenic: formed by external action.

Extrinsic erosion: that produced by agents from outside (the Moon).

Extrusion feature: one that was formed by the squeezing out of lava.

Fines: particles of the lunar regolith smaller than about 1 mm across. A cloud of fines generated by the motion of a NASA Roving Vehicle, on the Moon in 1972, is shown on the front cover.

Fissure: used here for a major fracture that has split open to leave a chasm or cleft.

Flow, laminar: well-ordered layered, or streamline, flow.

Flow ridging: characteristic, usually curved, ridges found on a congealing lava crust.

Flow, turbulent: flow in violent, eddying motion

Geomorphology: the study of the evolution and origin of features of an Earth-like body.

Ghost craters: see "elementary rings".

Goniphotometer: a photometer capable of measuring the intensity of light scattered from a specimen over a range of directions.

Graben feature: depressed terrain bounded by faults.

GRAIL: Gravity Recovery And Interior Laboratory.

Grid system: a Moon-wide fracture system revealed, on the surface, as respective families of lineaments.

GSFC: Goddard Space Flight Center.

Half-life: the time that has elapsed when half the initial mass of a substance has been lost as a result of radioactive decay.

ICI: Imperial Chemical Industries.

Ilmenite: titanium oxides.

Index of dispersion: V is the sum of $(N_i–N)^2$ for all values of i between 1 and r, divided by r–1, all divided by N; where N_i is the respective number of crater centres counted within each of r strips (see text) and, for a given position of the set of strips, N is calculated as the sum, for all values of i between 1 and r, of N_i/r (which is the mean number of craters per strip).

Indurated: hardened, moreso than an already consolidated rock.

Isostatic process: the sub-vertical adjustment of landforms that lack hydrostatic balance.

Isotropic medium: one having the same physical properties in all directions within it.

JAXA: Japanese Aerospace Exploration Agency.

Joint: the surface within a rock that has suffered latent fracture; or the gap that has been created when a fracture opens opposing surfaces within a rock without there being any relative displacement between them.

JPL: Jet Propulsion Laboratory.

L: Lick Observatory.

Lacus Mortis (Latin): the Lake of Death.

Levées: congealed edges of a lava flow.

Lineament: any linear feature of a planetary surface, be it a ridge, trough or crater -chain.

Lithosphere: the outer, rocky layer of a planet.

L.O: Lunar Orbiter spacecraft.

L.P.U: Lunar and Planetary Unit.

L.R.O: Lunar Reconnaissance Orbiter spacecraft.

Lunabase: a dark area, probably of lava, anywhere on the lunar surface.

M: MacDonald Observatory.

Magma: molten rock beneath the surface of a planet.

Mare (Latin, pron. Mar-uh: sea; (pl. maria, pron. Mar-reea).

Marebase: the dark, basic lavas of the maria.

Mare Cognitum (Latin): the Sea of Knowledge.

Mare Fecunditatis (Latin): the Sea of Fertility.

Mare Frigoris (Latin): the Sea of Cold.

Mare Humorum (Latin): the Sea of Mists.

Mare Imbrium (Latin): the Sea of Showers.

Mare Nectaris (Latin): the Sea of Nectar.

Mare Orientale (Latin): the Eastern Sea.

Mare Smythii (Latin): the Sea of Smyth.

Mare Tranquillitatis (Latin): the Sea of Tranquillity.

Maria: see "mare"

Mascons: concentrations of mass beneath the lunar surface.

Mass wasting: the natural shifting of material downslope.

Meteoroid: a naturally occurring, unnamed small object in space. One that has reached the Earth's surface is referred to as a meteorite.

Microdensitometer: an optical instrument used for measuring the density of small parts of a photographic emulsion.

Micrometeoroids: small meteoroids.

Microphotometer: an optical instrument used to measure the amount of light passing through parts of a transparency or reflected from parts of an opaque specimen.

NASA: National Aeronautics and Space Administration.

NERC: Natural Environment Research Council.

Nuée ardente: a fiery cloud of ash and pyroclasts erupted from a volcanic centre as a hot avalanche.

Number density: the number of features, or points representing them, per unit area of a surface.

Oceanus Procellarum (Latin): Ocean of Storms. The most extensive area of luna-base/lava on the Moon.

Outcrop: a rock unit that is exposed on, or an intrusion that has reached, the surface of a planet.

Outgassed rock: one that has lost some, or all, of its gaseous content.

Penumbral effects: since a lunar eminence that is illuminated by the Sun casts a shadow that exhibits an umbra and a penumbra, there can be an uncertainty in the position of the end of the shadow. (Other effects, such as terrain roughness, can add to this uncertainty.)

Perigee: the position, in the Moon's orbit, that is the nearest to the Earth.

Photogeology: the study of geology using photographs.

Plagioclase: a mineral common in lunar basic igneous rocks.

Planimeter: an instrument used to measure specific areas of a map, photograph, or diagram.

Proton accelerator: a machine for accelerating protons.

Proto-planet: an object formed early in the process of planetary formation.

Pyroclasts: igneous rock fragments ejected from a volcanic centre.

Radioactive substance: one which discharges atomic particles spontaneously and unpredictably.

Ray-elements: components of rays that commonly take the form of unidirectional streaks associated with secondary craters.

Rays, lunar: systems of lighter or darker streaks, each of which is associated with a primary crater and radiate from it.

Reflector (in astronomy): a telescope that has a primary mirror to collect and help to focus light.

Refractor (in astronomy): a telescope that utilises a primary lens to collect and (help to) focus light.

Regolith: lunar soil; the uppermost layer of fragmental and particulate rock, its thickness and degree of consolidation varying from place to place.

Repose, angle of: see "angle".

Rheometer: a device that can be used to measure the viscosity of a fliud.

Rhyolite: an acidic, fine-grained, lava.

Richter scale: a scale of magnitudes of quakes that is <3 for feeble events and increases to >8 in cases of highly destructive events.

Rille: trench-like feature of the lunar surface. Normal and arcuate rilles arise in fractures. Sinuous rilles derive from volcanic flows.

Rima (Latin): rille.

Ring dyke: a dyke that tends to the circular shape when viewed in plan or horizontal cross-section.

Ringwall: the sub-circular wall that surrounds, or part envelops, a crater.

Rock wastage: see "mass wasting".

Roscosmos: Russian State Corporation for State Activities/Federal Space Agency

Rose diagram: a graph, centred on a point, drawn through 360°.

Scree: an accumulation of rock fragments below the top of a cliff or other eminence from which the fragments have been detached.

Secondary impact craters: those smaller craters produced as a result of throwout from a larger impact crater (or as a result of bombs from an explosive or volcanic crater).

Secular acceleration: long-term acceleration.

Seismometer: a device to detect the vibrations in planetary bodies, usually in each of three mutually perpendicular directions.

Selenofaults: major faults that directly affect lunar relief over large distances.

Selenography: lunar geography.

Selenology: lunar geology.

Selenotectonics: tectonics applied to the Moon.

Septa: natural landforms, usually linear, that act as divisions between other surface features.

Sill: sub-horizontal igneous intrusion (that can appear as an outcrop) of sheet form.

Sinus Aestuum (Latin): Summer Bay.

Sinus Iridum(Latin): Rainbow Bay.

Sinus Medii (Latin): Middle Bay.

Sinus Roris (Latin): Bay of Dew

Slip line: in tectonics theory, slip lines may be calculated and charted as predictors of joint and fracture directions.

Stratigraphic sequence: the chronological sequence in which successive strata are laid down.

Strike of fault: the bearing of a fault.

Sub-circular: approximating to the circular form.

Sub-radial: departing from the radial direction.

Synchronous rotation: state of a planetary satellite when its axial rotation and orbital revolution have essentially the same period, so that essentially the same side of the satellite faces the planet permanently.

Tectonics: the study of the structural deformation of a planet, especially its crust.

Tertiary: the geological time period spanning the last seventy million years.

Time-lapse photographs: in the present context, those taken at fixed intervals of time but with longer intervals than those of normal cine photographs.

Trace (in geology): a line in the plan view of a surface to indicate the position and extent of a linear feature.

Turbulent flow: see "flow".

Upthrow: see "downthrow".

USAF: United States Air Force

W: Mount Wilson and Palomar Observatories.

Wrinkle ridge: a snaking ridge found in the marebase. Although "mare ridge" is commonly used synonymously with "wrinkle ridge", the latter designation is of more general use since the ridges are not exclusive to maria.

Y: Yerkes Observatory.

Index

ages of lunar lavas, 77, 78
Airy, 53
Aldrin, E. ("Buzz"), 1, 3, 69, 209
Alphonsus, 68, 70, 161, 162
Alter, D., 17, 22
Anderson, E., 7
Andrews-Hanna, J., 151
angle: dihedral, 50; internal friction, 44; repose, of regolith, 78, 79
anorthosite, 63, 115; age of, 63
Apollo 11, 3, 42, 63, 209
Apollo 12, 42
Apollo 14, 42
Apollo 15, 28, 42, 63
Apollo 16, 42, 63, 89, 170, 187, 202
Apollo 17, 63, 209
Arago, 189, 190
Argelander, 53
Ardnamurchan, 193
Aristarchus, 77, 115, 116, 118, 119, 121, 122, 129, 139–141, 145–147, 161, 203
Aristillus, 158, 181, 184, 186
Aristoteles, 160
Armstrong, N., 1, 69, 209
Arran, 193
Ashbrook, J., 22
ash flow/ignimbrite, 168
Avicenna, 202

Bailly A and B, 202
Baldwin, R., 1, 2, 133, 177
Barr, E., 161
basalts, 64, 99
base surge, 115, 137, 146
Battleship Rock, 84, 88
Boeing Aircraft Corporation, 99
Boscovitch, 56
British Astronomical Association, Lunar
    Section, 82
Boulton, G., 170
Buji ring complex, 196
Bullialdus, 181
Bushveld Complex, 198

Carlingford, 193
cauldron subsidence, 193
Cayley/Descartes region, 63
cine/time-lapse photography, 11, 17
Clavius, 113, 199, 200, 201, 203
Clementine spacecraft, 177
Chevrel, M., 172
cone sheets, 193, 195
Copernican period, 146, 147
Copernicus, 28, 115–117, 129, 136, 143, 144, 203, 204
Craters, lunar: benches, 109; bright, 90, 91, 107, 108; central blocks, 133, 137; central peaks, 4, 133–137; chains, 81, 83, 85, 97, 102, 113, 173, 203; clustering, 97, 98, 112; concentration near equator, 91; counts, 81, 86, 87, 95, 102; dark halo, 115, 117, 147; deltoids, 119; distorted, 39, 41, 42; distribution, 90, 102, 104, 112; dot maps, 90, 93; endogenic and exogenic, 81, 85, 91, 93, 99, 104, 111, 112; eumorphic, 107; explosion, 4, 8, 9, 25, 81, 83, 109; graben, 113; impact, 81, 85, 90, 107, 112, 119; interlocking, 200; models, 39, 41, 42; number-densities, 86, 87, 103, 104; origins of large, 113, 115–119, 149, 162, 205–207; origins of small, 81, 85, 94, 203; plastic deformation around, 119; plateau, 206; polygonal, 113, 199; proportions of internal to external, 95, 104, 111, 112; populations, 86; ray, 115–119; rock blocks in, 108, 109; saturation cratering, 86, 89, 205; secondary, 8, 81, 204; shapes of small, 112; small double, 107–109; statistics, 85; submorphic, 111; vents, 167; volcanic and volcanic flows in, 121–124, 149
Crimean Astrophysical Observatory, 161

Darney, M., 25
Darwin, G., 65
dating by crater counts, 95
Deer, W., 7
Delisle, 83
de Vico A, 155
distance between Earth and Moon, 63, 65
domes, volcanic, 126, 127, 189–191
Donati, 53
dykes, 81, 82, 139, 151–153, 156, 166, 193, 195

225

Earth and Moon orbital parameters, 34
Earth: orbit, 31, 32; slowing rotation speed, 31–33, 37; tides, 31–33, 37
Egede, 181, 182
elasticity, planetary, 57
Elegante, 83–85
elementary rings: distribution, 181, 183; melting of, 183, 186
Elger, T., 4
Elston, W., 84, 113, 195–197
endocraters (endogenic craters) *see* Craters, lunar
Eratosthenes, 203
erosion and denudation; extrinsic, 77, 78; intrinsic, 78; rate, on Moon, 78, 111
Ettenfield, D., 90
Euler, 157, 159
europium anomalies, 63, 64
exotic rock, 63
Ezersky, V., 161

faults, 17–22, 43, 53–57, 153, 190; Cauchy, 57; complex, 55, 57; graben, 53, 54; near Arago, 189, 190; selenofaults, 52, 53; types, 19
fiammées, 84, 88
Flamsteed P., 181–183, 185, 187, 202
flows, lava; *see also* lavas; channel in, 173; dating mare flows, 111; flow ridging, 121, 123; laminar and turbulent, 172; levées, 169; units, 102, 103
fractures: around an explosion crater, 157; caused by impacts, 150; depths, 44, 150; in floors of craters, 131–134, 140, 144, 149; in tumuli, 150; in upper parts of Moon, 150
frictional heating: by tides, 63; by isostasy, 149
Fryer, R., 49, 86, 87, 93

Galland, O., 196
Gash, P., 59, 60, 76, 113
ghost craters/rings; *see also* elementary rings; , 181, 202
chains, 191; polygonal walls, 181
Gilbert, G., 25, 29
Giodano Bruno, 147
Gold, T., 136
goniphotometer, 67, 70
GRAIL, 151, 160, 177
Greenacre, J., 161
grid system, 43, 45, 48, 97, 133, 144, 167; fine lineaments, 67, 68; gross lineaments, 43–48; origin, 59, 65, 205; volcanic vents influenced by grid, 126
gravity anomalies, 151; *see also* mascons
Guest, J., 67, 190

Hapke, B., 67
Hartmann, W., 65
Hawaii, 87, 99, 127, 131, 194
Hayne, P., 129
Head, J., 206

heat flow from interior of Moon, 63
heat of accumulation, 65
Hedin, 153
Henry, J., 129
Herring, A., 86
Herschel, W., 161
Holmes, A., 7, 193, 194
Hubble Advance Camera for Surveys, 140
Hulme, G., 149, 150, 168, 169, 172, 179
Humboldt, 206, 207
Hurwitz, D., 176

ilmenite (lunar), 140, 209
impact craters, 81; formation of, 136; gardening, 78; melts, 77; velocities of impact, 177, 178
Imperial Chemical Industries Nobel Division, 8
index of dispersion, 93–95, 111, 217
interlocking ringwalls, 200–202
International Space Station, 211
intrusions, volcanic, 151
Irwin, J., 68
isostatic recovery, 133, 136, 149

Jackson, 147
Jeffreys, H., 205
jetting, 136
Jodrell Bank, 9
joints in rocks, 43

Kaguya spacecraft, 177
Kalinyak, A., 161
Kamionko, L., 161
Kiang, T., 14
Kilauea, 131; convection cells in lava, 131; fractures in lava crust, 131, 132
King, 89
King, E., 136
Kodak (Eastman Kodak Company), 10
Kopal, Z., 7
Kosyrev, N., 161, 162
Kuiper, G., 14, 67, 81, 86, 210
Kunowski, 202

Lacus Mortis, 54, 55, 57
Lade, 207
Lambert, 181, 185
Lamont, 189–191
lavas, lunar, 100–102; ages, 63, 77, 78, 145, 146; depths of origin, 150; differentiation, 129; flow fronts, 101–103; flows, 101, 111, 121–124, 145, 165, 169, 174; fountaining, 173; froth, 69, 102; lakes, 123, 124; origin, 28, 149, 205; outgassed, 67, 69, 133; radar reflective, 129; reflectivities, 163; tubes, 102; tumuli, 125; viscosities, 99, 170
Letronne, 186, 187
Lick Observatory, 1, 4
Liebig F, 56

light scattering by Moon, 67
lineaments, 25–29, 39, 40, 43, 81, 94, 97; bundles, 157, 159, 160; dihedral angles between, 50; fine, 67–75, 78; gross, 61, 207; in central mountains of craters, 135; in floor of Tycho, 126; in lake and central mountains of Tycho, 135; in Rima Hadley, 170; in Mt. Hadley, 73; origin of gross, 61, 157, 158; polar, 60; randomised, 163; rose diagram, 49, 50; sub-radial, 156, 166, 177
Lovell, Sir Bernard, 9
lunabase, 163
Lunar and Planetary Laboratory, 67, 81, 86, 121
Lunar and Planetary Unit, 45, 59
lunar crustal tensions, 153
lunar module, 3
Lunar Orbiter, 45, 48, 68, 86, 87, 99, 100, 121, 133, 134, 139, 143, 177
Lunar Prospector, 140, 177
Lunar Reconnaissance Orbiter, 133–135, 139, 140, 177, 207, 208
lunar shadows, 1, 2
Luna 3, 43

MacCaulay, J., 84
Mädler, J., 135, 136, 203
magma: chambers, 193, 199; elongated chambers, 199; tidal action on magmas in chambers, 199; viscosity, 196
magmatic intrusion, 133, 178, 180
Marcus, A., 85
Mare: Cognitum, 67, 68; Crisium, 153; Foecunditatis/Fecunditatis, 86; Frigoris, 86, 95; Humorum, 56, 95, 177, 207; Imbrium, 13, 25, 26, 28, 29, 43, 75, 97, 100, 101, 111, 163–165, 173, 177–179; Nectaris, 177, 203; Nubium, 181; Orientale, 86, 163–166, 177, 178; Serenitatis, 13, 179; Smythii, 86; Tranquillitatis, 1, 63, 74, 86, 189, 209
maria, origin of circular, 177, 205
Mars, 209, 211
mascons, 165, 177–180, 181
mass wasting, 143
Mattingly, K., 89
Mauna Loa, 102, 194
Meteor Crater, 83–85
meteoroids: early bombardment of Moon, 77; high velocity, 4, 149; minor impacts, 67, 77; origin of, 77
Mogollon ring complex, 196, 198
Moon: acceleration, 31, 32; accumulation, 65, 205; atmospheric pressure, 81; colony, 209; convection, 206; crustal tensions, 51; crustal thickness, 180; density distribution, 205; differentiation, 206; distance from Earth, 63; far side, 177, 179; full, 1, 2; geological samples, 211, 212; gravity, 102; ilmenite, 212; industry, 211; mantle expansion, 160, 178; melting, 63, 205; micrometeoroids, 211; origin, 65; plants, 210; power generation, 209; quarrying, 212;

radiation hazards, 210; recession from Earth, 37; rotation, 43, 205; stress fields, 42, 157, 159, 160; transcient events, 161; volcanic activity, 140, 161, 162; weather forecasting, 210
Moon Crater, 83, 86
moonquakes, 43, 77, 111; strength, 150
Moore, Sir Patrick, 2
mountains, lunar: Alps, 68, 73; Altai, 54, 55, 207; Apennines, 13, 203; Caucasus, 13; Cordillera, 166; Hadley, 68, 73; Jura, 163; La Hire, 173; Taurus, 209
Mount Wilson Observatory, 4
Mourne, 193
Mull, 193
Muller, P., 177, 179
Murray, J., 111, 112

Natural Environment Research Council, 45, 49
Nernst and Nernst T, 200, 201, 203
nuée ardente, 168

oblate spheroid, 58
Oceanus Procellarum, 95, 163, 175, 202
O'Keefe, J., 183
origin of the Moon, 65

partial melting in the Moon, 63, 64
Pettengill, G., 129
Pic-du-Midi Observatory, 8, 10, 11, 13, 17
Pinnacate region of Mexico, 83, 101
Pinkerton, H., 170
plagioclase, 63, 65
Plato, 95
Porter, 200, 201
potassium, lunar, 209
Prinz, 68, 72
Proclus, 147
proton bombardment, 67
Ptolemaeus, 89, 113
pyroclasts, 209

radar, ground penetrating, 204, 211
radioactive elements in Moon, 64
radon, 140
Ranger 7, 67
Ranger 9, 68
ray craters, 2, 68, 115–119
ray elements, 115, 117, 143
ray systems' lifetime, 78
Regiomontanus, 43, 46
regolith, 67, 76, 129; cohesion, 78, 79; compaction, 109; drainage, 102, 173; generation, 78; shallow channels in, 102; thickness, 109, 129, 156; water in, 210
rheometer, 170
Rhum, 193
Rilles (Rimae); *see also* sinuous rilles, 41, 56, 57, 153, 156, 157, 165, 167, 169–171, 176

ring dykes and complexes, 195–197; lunar, 199
Ritter, 200
Roche, E., 65
Rogers, P., 67, 69
rotational stressing of Moon, 59–61, 199
rotation/spin, synchronous and free, 31, 57–59;
synchronicity, establishment of, 65
Rum, 193, 194
Runcorn, K., 33, 68
Rutherford, 201
Rutherford, E., 7

Sabine, 190, 200
Safety in Mines Research Establishment, 8
San Francisco Volcanic Field, 175
Schmidt, 200
Schmidt, H., 209
Schröter's Valley, 168, 171
seeing disc, 11, 12
seismicity, 78
seismometry, 64, 150
selenofaults, 52, 53
selenography, 2
selenology, 4
shadow lengths on Moon, 17
shock front, 137
Shoemaker, E., 83
Short, N., 150
Shorthill, R., 129
sinuous rilles, 167–172, 174, 175
Sinus Roris, 172
Sinus Iridum, 27, 28, 163
Sinus Medii, 86, 95
Sirsalis Rille, 153–155
Sjogren, W., 177
Skye, 193
Slieve Gullion, 193
slip-lines, 47, 51
sodium, lunar, 209
solar radiation damage to lunar rocks, 67
south pole to Aitken depression, 177, 179
Spurr, J., 4, 113
Stadius, 203, 204
Straight Wall, 17–19, 21, 22, 54
stratigraphy, inversion, 4
strike-slip faults, 43, 45, 46
Strom, R., 77, 121, 124, 133, 149, 168
Sunset Crater National Monument, 82
Surtsey active lava flow front, 101
spin see rotation

Surveyor VII, 63, 64, 75, 79, 115
Surveyor soft-landers, 68
systems A, B, C, D and R_i, 43, 44, 49, 97

Taruntius, 181, 186
tensions in the Moon, 51, 156, 160
terrestrial volcanism and ring complexes, 193–198
Tertiary ring complexes, 193
Theia, 65
Thorarinsson, S., 101
tidal heating, 64, 205
tidal stressing of Moon, 59–61, 63, 76, 199
Timocharis, 157
titanium, lunar, 209
Titulaer, C., 86
Todhunter, R., 100
Tresca's yield condition, 164
Tsiolkovski, 40, 95
turbulent lava flows, 168–170, 174
Tycho, 63, 68, 71, 77, 115, 121–126, 129, 131, 136,
    149, 150, 156, 162, 168, 181, 203, 206;
floor fractures, 131, 132; fractures near feet of
central mountains, 133

United States Geological Survey, Flagstaff, 83
Urey, H., 1, 4, 27, 33, 210

Valles Caldera, 84, 88
Vaniman, D., 210
Vesuvius, 194
Vitello, 206
Vogel, 53, 54
volcanic edifices on Moon, 81

Wargentin, 207, 208
Warner, B., 156, 160, 203, 204
water/ice, lunar, 210
Wells, M., 25
Whitaker, E., 82, 84
Wilmarth, V., 83
Wilson, L., 67, 69, 181, 186, 206
Wise, B., 86
Wolf T (lunar feature), 181, 184, 186
wrinkle ridges, 13–15, 182, 185, 190, 191, 202, 204,
    207, 208

Young, J., 74

Zimbabwe, 198
Zwicky, F., 210